THE WBA QUIZ BOOK

COMPILED BY MART MATTHEWS

INTRODUCTION

Hello Baggies fans everywhere and welcome to what I hope
is the most comprehensive quiz on your club on the market.

A word about the League Cup is required here. It has had so many
sponsors over the years that in this book I've simply called it the
League Cup throughout.

My choice of 12 Top Throstles may not totally chime with yours,
but if it provokes debate that's all to the good. I hope you enjoy it.

ACKNOWLEDGEMENT

My thanks to Pat Morgan again for his excellent work
in preparing the manuscript for publication.

Published by G2 Entertainment Ltd
© G2 Entertainment 2023

ISBN: 9781782815600

PICTURE CREDITS: Action Images, Alamy

THE WBA QUIZ BOOK

1. ALBION'S EUROPEAN ADVENTURES
2. ALBION V ASTON VILLA: CUP COMPETITIONS
3. ALBION V ASTON VILLA: LEAGUE
4. ALBION V BIRMINGHAM CITY: CUP COMPETITIONS
5. ALBION V BIRMINGHAM CITY: LEAGUE
6. ALBION V WOLVES: CUP COMPETITIONS
7. ALBION V WOLVES: LEAGUE
8. ANYTHING GOES
9. BIRTHPLACES
10. CHRISTMAS CRACKERS
11. CRYPTIC ALBION PART 1
12. CRYPTIC ALBION PART 2
13. CUP FINAL MEN PART 1 BEFORE THE ALBION
14. CUP FINAL MEN PART 2 AFTER THE ALBION
15. EDIBLE ALBION
16. FA CUP FINALS PART 1
17. FA CUP FINALS PART 2
18. FA CUP SEMI-FINALS
19. FLORA, FAUNA, FISH AND FOWL
20. THE FOREIGN LEGION PART 1
21. THE FOREIGN LEGION PART 2
22. GOALKEEPERS PART 1
23. GOALKEEPERS PART 2
24. HELPING HANDS 1946-2000
25. HELPING HANDS 2000-2023
26. HOMES OF THE ALBION
27. INTERNATIONALS: ENGLAND (POST-SECOND WORLD WAR)
28. INTERNATIONALS: NORTHERN IRELAND (POST-SECOND WORLD WAR)
29. INTERNATIONALS: REPUBLIC OF IRELAND (POST-SECOND WORLD WAR)
30. INTERNATIONALS: SCOTLAND (POST-SECOND WORLD WAR)
31. INTERNATIONALS: WALES (POST-SECOND WORLD WAR)
32. LEAGUE CUP FINALS
33. MANAGERS PART 1
34. MANAGERS PART 2
35. OPENING DAYS
36. OTHER COMPETITIONS
37. PENALTY SHOOT-OUTS
38. PLAY-OFFS
39. POT LUCK
40. RED CARDS
41. TRANSFERS 1888-1939
42. TRANSFERS 1946-1960
43. TRANSFERS 1960-1975
44. TRANSFERS 1975-1990
45. TRANSFERS 1990-2005
46. TRANSFERS 2005-2020
47. 12 TOP THROSTLES NO 1: RONNIE ALLEN
48. 12 TOP THROSTLES NO 2: JEFF ASTLE
49. 12 TOP THROSTLES NO 3: BILLY BASSETT
50. 12 TOP THROSTLES NO 4: TONY BROWN
51. 12 TOP THROSTLES NO 5: TOMMY GLIDDEN
52. 12 TOP THROSTLES NO 6: DEREK KEVAN

CONTENTS

53. 12 TOP THROSTLES
NO 7: CYRILLE REGIS

54. 12 TOP THROSTLES
NO 8: WG RICHARDSON

55. 12 TOP THROSTLES
NO 9: BOBBY ROBSON

56. 12 TOP THROSTLES
NO 10: BRYAN ROBSON

57. 12 TOP THROSTLES
NO 11: BOB TAYLOR

58. 12 TOP THROSTLES
NO 12: JOHN WILE

59. VENUES

60. ALBION IN THE FA CUP 1883-1915

61. ALBION IN THE FA CUP 1919-1939

62. ALBION IN THE FA CUP 1946-1960

63. ALBION IN CUP COMPETITIONS
1960-1970

64. ALBION IN CUP COMPETITIONS
1970-1980

65. ALBION IN CUP COMPETITIONS
1980-1990

66. ALBION IN CUP COMPETITIONS
1990-2000

67. ALBION IN THE FOOTBALL LEAGUE
1888-1900

68. ALBION IN THE FOOTBALL LEAGUE
1900-1915

69. ALBION IN THE FOOTBALL LEAGUE
1919-1930

70. ALBION IN THE FOOTBALL LEAGUE
1930-1939

71. ALBION IN THE FOOTBALL LEAGUE
1946-1960

72. ALBION IN THE FOOTBALL LEAGUE
1960-1970

73. ALBION IN THE FOOTBALL LEAGUE
1970-1980

74. ALBION IN THE FOOTBALL LEAGUE
1980-1990

75. ALBION IN THE FOOTBALL LEAGUE
1990-2000

76. ALBION SEASON 2000-2001

77. ALBION SEASON 2001-2002

78. ALBION SEASON 2002-2003

79. ALBION SEASON 2003-2004

80. ALBION SEASON 2004-2005

81. ALBION SEASON 2005-2006

82. ALBION SEASON 2006-2007

83. ALBION SEASON 2007-2008

84. ALBION SEASON 2008-2009

85. ALBION SEASON 2009-2010

86. ALBION SEASON 2010-2011

87. ALBION SEASON 2011-2012

88. ALBION SEASON 2012-2013

89. ALBION SEASON 2013-2014

90. ALBION SEASON 2014-2015

91. ALBION SEASON 2015-2016

92. ALBION SEASON 2016-2017

93. ALBION SEASON 2017-2018

94. ALBION SEASON 2018-2019

95. ALBION SEASON 2019-2020

96. ALBION SEASON 2020-2021

97. ALBION SEASON 2021-2022

98. ALBION SEASON 2022-2023

99. WHERE DID YOU COME FROM?

100. WILD CARD

ALBION'S EUROPEAN ADVENTURES

Between 1966 and 1981, West Bromwich Albion competed in Europe in five seasons. They had three outings in the UEFA Cup and one each in the Inter-Cities Fairs Cup and the European Cup Winners' Cup.

1.   Between 1966 and 1981, Albion participated in 11 two-legged ties. What was statistically unusual about all of them?

2.   Who scored West Brom's first goal in Europe when they drew 1-1 away to DOS Utrecht of the Netherlands in the first leg of the Fairs Cup on 2 November 1966?
A. Jeff Astle B. Bobby Hope C. John Kaye D. Graham Lovett

3.   Who is the only player to score in three successive European matches for West Bromwich Albion when he did so at home and away to Bruges and away to Dinamo Bucharest in the European Cup Winners' Cup in the autumn of 1968?

4.   When Albion beat Galatasaray of Turkey in the 1978-79 UEFA Cup, it provided the only occasion in their European exploits when the home and away scores were the same. By what score did they win both matches?
A. 1-0 B. 2-0 C. 2-1 D. 3-1

5.   Who were the only two players to score from the penalty spot for West Brom in Europe?

6.   Which Scottish club knocked Albion out of the European Cup Winners' Cup at the quarter-final stage in 1968-69?

7.   In that tie one surname could be found on both teams. What was it?

8.   Who scored the Baggies' last goal in Europe when they lost 3-1 at home to Grasshoppers of Zurich in the UEFA Cup on 30 September 1981?
A. David Mills B. Gary Owen C. Cyrille Regis D. Alistair Robertson

9.   Who was responsible for Albion's only European hat-trick when they beat DOS Utrecht 5-2 at the Hawthorns in the Fairs Cup on 9 November 1966?

10.   Apart from reaching that European Winners' Cup quarter-final in 1968-69, the only other time Albion got that far was in the UEFA Cup of 1978-79, when they lost 2-1 on aggregate to which club from eastern Europe?

ALBION V ASTON VILLA: CUP COMPETITIONS 2

11. West Bromwich Albion and Aston Villa have met each other in the FA Cup on seven grounds. The Hawthorns and Villa Park obviously constitute two of them. What are the other five?

12. Who is the only Albion player to score in two FA Cup ties against Aston Villa, doing so in the successive seasons of 1924-25 and 1925-26?

13. Who was the last man to score against Aston Villa in an FA Cup tie between the clubs?

14. In 1895, West Brom and Aston Villa made history by becoming the first two clubs to play against each other in three FA Cup finals. That record lasted over 100 years, but now four finals have occurred that number of times. Which ones were they?

15. Albion have done much better against Villa in the League Cup than in the FA Cup, claiming twice Villa's total of ties won. They met each other for the first time in the competition on 17 November 1965, when Albion won 3-1 in front of a 40,000-plus crowd at the Hawthorns. Which player got two of their three that night?
A. Jeff Astle B. Tony Brown C. Clive Clark D. John Kaye

16. The following season it must have given Albion's players, as reigning League Cup holders, great pleasure to meet Villa again and register a 6-1 win at the Hawthorns in their first game in defence of the trophy. Who scored the only West Bromwich Albion hat-trick in a cup tie against Aston Villa that night?

17. On 3 September 1969, Albion made it a trio of League Cup victories over Aston Villa when they won at Villa Park for the first time in the competition, by 2-1. Who scored their goals that night?
A. Astle and Brown B. Hartford and Suggett C. Astle and Suggett
D. Hartford and Brown

18. On 20 December 1981, Albion went to Villa Park again in the same competition and made it four wins out of four since the League Cup started in 1960 by winning 1-0. Which defender's goal was the difference between the teams that night?

19. West Brom won the FA Cup in 1888, 1892, 1931, 1954 and 1968. After which one of those FA Cup victories did Aston Villa beat the Albion in the first game of the following year's competition?

20. There have been three replays between the clubs in cup competitions. They came in the FA Cup in 1924-25 and 1956-57 and in the League Cup in 1985-86. Which one of the three did Albion win?

3 ALBION V ASTON VILLA: LEAGUE

21. As founder members of the Football League, these two clubs played each other for the first time in the League in the 1888-89 season. Albion drew 3-3 at home that season and beat Villa 3-2 in 1892-93. Which prolific goalscorer, who was also the first player to score a League hat-trick for Albion, scored twice in both matches?

22. Who scored the last 20th century goal registered by Albion in the League against Aston Villa?
A. Steve Hunt B. Steve MacKenzie C. Andy Thompson D. Imre Varadi

23. What have Bob Pailor and George James done that nobody else in Albion's colours has done?

24. Villa were relegated for the first time in their history in 1935-36 and, although Albion contrived to lose 3-0 to them at the Hawthorns on, appropriately, April Fool's Day, they had already recorded their biggest win over them at Villa Park on 19 October 1935 – by what score?

25. Before the return to normality after the Second World War, Albion and Villa played in the Football League South in 1945-46. West Brom's 1-0 home win over Villa on 29 August 1945 came courtesy of a player who would go on to lift the FA Cup with the club in 1954. Who was he?

26. West Brom and Aston Villa met each other outside the top flight for the first time in 1973-74 with Albion enjoying the better of the exchanges, winning 2-0 at the Hawthorns on Boxing Day and 3-1 at Villa Park on 2 March 1974. Who scored four of Albion's five goals in those games?

27. What is the longest number of seasons in a row in which there has been no league match between the Baggies and Aston Villa?
A. 10 B. 12 C. 14 D. 16

28. When Villa beat West Brom 4-3 at Villa Park in the Premier League on 29 January 2014, which Villa midfielder scored for both sides?

29. There were a couple of battles between the clubs in the late 1950s when relegation hinged on the outcome, but perhaps their most important meeting was in the Championship play-off semi-final, played over two legs in May 2019. After being unfortunate to lose the first leg, Albion squared things with a 1-0 win in the second leg at the Hawthorns, before losing the eventual penalty shoot-out 4-1. Who scored Albion's winner on the night, and which two players who share the first letter of their surnames were unsuccessful in the shoot-out?

30. Who had lifted supporters' hopes by giving Albion the lead at Villa Park in the first game?

ALBION V BIRMINGHAM CITY: CUP COMPETITIONS 4

31. Whether as Small Heath, Birmingham or Birmingham City, their local rivals have contested eight FA Cup ties with Albion, who have lost just once when, in front of a crowd of 57,213 at the Hawthorns, City won 1-0 on their road to Wembley. In which season?

32. In all cup meetings between Albion and the Blues, the only time a particular scoreline appeared was in the League Cup on 30 October 1984 at St Andrew's. What was it?

33. It doesn't get much sweeter than beating Birmingham City in an FA Cup semi-final at Villa Park, and it has happened just once. In which season?

34. The usual suspects grabbed the goals in Albion's 2-0 win that day. Who were they?

35. The most recent meeting between the clubs in the FA Cup, in fact the only one this century, came at St Andrew's in the fourth round of the 2014-15 competition. How did the game end up?

36. Which front man scored twice for the Baggies that day?

37. Who was the last West Bromwich Albion player to find the Birmingham net twice in the FA Cup before that 2014-15 tie, and in what season?

38. The only time that the clubs have met each other in a cup replay was a successful occasion for West Brom, who won through 3-1 – in which competition and in what season?

39. In which competition did the clubs draw 2-2 at St Andrew's on 30 January 1996, with Albion coming out 4-1 winners on penalties?

40. Two players with surnames beginning with R got Albion's goals in that match. Who were they?

41. After a few meetings, some of them rather bitter affairs to say the least, when Birmingham still went under the name of Small Heath, the clubs played each other for the first time as West Bromwich Albion v Birmingham in Division Two on Boxing Day of 1908, in a game that finished 1-1 at the Hawthorns. Albion's first goal against Birmingham came from the penalty spot. Who scored it?
A. Fred Buck B. Bill Garraty C. Charlie Hewitt D. Jesse Pennington

42. Who was responsible for the first West Brom hat-trick against Birmingham, in a 5-1 win at the Hawthorns on 6 February 1926?
A. Joe Carter B. Stan Davies C. George James D. Charlie Wilson

43. What was unique about the 1923-24 season where the Albion v Birmingham derby was concerned?

44. Albion fans were in dreamland when they visited St Andrew's in the successive seasons of 1957-58, 1958-59 and 1959-60, because the scorelines were unbelievable and got progressively better. By what three scores did they win?

45. Which West Brom player scored six of the 18 registered at the home of the enemy?

46. Which Albion player scored in both games when they did the Football League double over Birmingham City (1-0 away and 3-1 at home) in the 1963-64 season, and then for good measure scored Albion's goal in a 1-1 St Andrew's draw the following season, all three matches taking place in September? A. Clive Clark B. Ronnie Fenton C. Ken Foggo D. John Kaye

47. In 1985-86 the clubs were relegated together from Division One, but West Brom did have the silver lining of a league double over their rivals, winning 1-0 away and 2-1 at home. At the Hawthorns on 19 October 1985, the two Albion scorers shared the first letter of their names. Who were they?

48. In the 1990s the clubs met each other for the first time in the third tier of English football, while in the next century they played against each other in the Premier League for the first time. Which two seasons were they?

49. West Brom and Birmingham City's experience of each other in the new century was often like ships passing in the night as they went up and down the leagues. In 2010-11, Albion's two wins by the same scoreline helped to relegate their rivals from the Premier League. By what score did they win both matches?

50. The clubs met again in the Championship in 2018-19 and 2019-20, with Albion winning 3-2 at home in the first of those seasons and 3-2 away in the latter. Who scored their 74th-minute winner in the home game, and which player turned the second game on its head with goals in the 73rd and 81st minutes?

ALBION V WOLVES: CUP COMPETITIONS

51. Which surname can be found twice among West Brom goalscorers in FA Cup ties against Wolves, first in the 1880s and then again in the 1920s?

52. Amazingly, Albion and Wolves have managed to avoid each other in over 60 years of the League Cup, but Albion have a superb record against their great Black Country rivals in the FA Cup. What is the win, lose, draw situation in their ten meetings in that competition?

53. In their ten FA Cup meetings, the clubs have played on three grounds. What are they and can you place them in order on the basis of the number of games they have hosted?

54. In a record that still stands, who became the only West Bromwich Albion man to score twice in an FA Cup tie against Wolves when he got both goals in their 2-1 fourth round win at Molineux on 27 January 1962?

55. West Brom won the FA Cup in 1888, 1892, 1931, 1954 and 1968. In which two of those years did they go on to win it after knocking out Wolves?

56. In what season did Albion and Wolves last play each other in an FA Cup tie at the Hawthorns?

57. West Brom and Wolves have never contested an FA Cup semi-final, but what is the highest round in the competition in which they have met each other?

58. The only time the clubs have played each other in the FA Cup this century proved to be a great day for Baggies fans as Albion won 3-0 at Molineux in the fourth round of 2006-07. Their goals came from two forwards and a midfielder. Who were they?

59. A colour scored for West Brom against Wolves in their first FA Cup meeting in 1886, while one of their goals in their 2-0 replay win at Molineux in 1924 came from the cockney rhyming slang for 'neck'. Finally, a winged monster with an eagle's head and a lion's body found the net for the Throstles against Wolves when they won a third round tie at Molineux on 7 January 1956. Who were the three players, who share the first letter of their names?

60. Albion have scored over three times as many goals as Wolves in their FA Cup contests down the years, while the latter have never scored more than once in any cup tie against the Baggies. True or false?

61. Albion and Wolves, as near neighbours and among the 12 founder members of the Football League in 1888, saw a lot of each other early in proceedings, and the new century had arrived before there was a season in which they failed to meet. Wolves had the better of the early skirmishes with five wins and a draw in the first six fixtures, but West Brom made up for all that in one stunning display at the recently opened Molineux on 27 December 1893 by giving Wolves the worst hammering on home soil they have had to this day. What was the score?

62. The most goals the clubs have shared in a league game is ten. This time it was one day later, on 28 December, but the year was 1929 and the venue was the Hawthorns. What was the score?

63. The 1951-52 season was at the start of a golden period of intense competition between the two clubs, and they met on consecutive days over Easter on 14 and 15 April, with Albion coming out on top 2-1 at home and 4-1 away. Which Albion forward scored in both matches?
A. Ronnie Allen B. Frank Griffin C. George Lee D. Johnny Nicholls

64. One Albion forward had a great time against Wolves between 1957 and 1962, scoring WBA's only goal against them in the two games of 1957-58 and then finding the net home and away in 1958-59, 60-61 and 61-62. Who was he?

65. In 1981-82, Wolves were relegated with Albion four points better off them at the death. It was just as well they beat the old rivals 3-0 and 2-1, or they would have gone through the trapdoor instead. Who scored in both games?

66. The first time the clubs met in a Football League game in the 21st century was on 17 October 2000, when the derby at the Hawthorns was decided in Albion's favour with the only goal of the game coming from the penalty spot. Who took the penalty?

67. In 2001-02, West Bromwich Albion gained automatic promotion to the Premier League and Wolves lost out to, of all teams, Birmingham City in the play-offs. There were just three points between them and so Albion's 1-0 win at Molineux on 2 December 2001 was crucial. Who got the vital goal?
A. Danny Dichio B. Scott Dobie C. Jordão D. Bob Taylor

68. It was an exciting few days in the Black Country when the clubs came up against each other in the Championship play-off semi-final over two legs in 2006-07, Albion going into the final after a 3-2 win at Molineux followed by a 1-0 second-leg victory. Who scored three of their four goals?

69. West Brom gave Wolves a helping hand to another relegation from the Premier League in the 2011-12 season, beating them 2-0 at home and 5-1 away. Who scored a hat-trick in the latter game on 12 February 2012?

70. After a long wait, battle was joined again in the Premier League when West Brom won 3-2 at Molineux on 16 January 2021. Semi Ajayi got one of Albion's goals but the other two came from the penalty spot, for which one man was entrusted with both kicks. He didn't miss. Who was he?

ANYTHING GOES

8

71. Albion were involved in an extremely rare if not unique situation on 16 March 2002, when their away game was brought to a halt in the 83rd minute because their opponents had been reduced to just six men. Albion led 3-0 at the time and the result stood - gainst which club?

72. When West Brom won the Football League for the only time in their history in 1919-20, only one club bettered their 35 home points by securing 36. Who were they? A. Burnley B. Chelsea C. Manchester City D. Sunderland

73. One of Albion's greatest goalscorers shares his surname with a player who scored for Argentina in the 1986 World Cup final. Who is the Albion player? A. Ronnie Allen B. Tony Brown C. Cyrille Regis D. Bob Taylor

74. The 1939-40 season was abandoned due to the outbreak of war after just three fixtures. Albion won 2-1 at Swansea, drew 3-3 at Coventry and then played their only game of the season at the Hawthorns on 2 September 1939, losing 4-3 at home to which London club?
A. Fulham B. Millwall C. Spurs D. West Ham United

75. This question concerns two excellent West Brom performances. The first came on 6 March 2016, when they beat Manchester United at the Hawthorns for the first time since 1984 with a 1-0 scoreline. The second was an FA Cup fourth round win against Liverpool at Anfield in the 2017-18 season. Albion were assisted in the first game by a red card for a Manchester United player and in the second by an own goal from a Liverpool player. The two players share the first three letters of their surnames and also have the same initials. Who are they?

76. For the 2011-12 season a new walkway outside the Hawthorns' East Stand was laid and named the Baggies Brick Road, with personalised bricks available for fans to buy. Two celebrity Albion fans laid the first bricks. Who were they?

77. What was unique in the history of West Bromwich Albion about the 1956-57 season?

78. Why did West Brom play in blue shirts rather than blue and white striped ones for the duration of the Second World War?

79. Who are the only club that Albion have beaten in more than one FA Cup final?

80. Why did West Brom wear white shirts and shorts for their home game with Leicester City on 11 April 2015, with shirts numbered two to 11 and no sponsor?

BIRTHPLACES

81. Clive Clark, Martin Dickinson and Don Goodman together played in more than 500 Football League games for the Throstles. From which city did they all hail?

82. Which city is home to Albion players Kevin Campbell, Laurie Cunningham, Danny Dichio, Tony Grealish, Jason Roberts, Imre Varadi and Chris Whyte?

83. Albion player Geoff Horsfield was born in a Yorkshire town that shares its name with someone who played just once for West Brom in the 1954-55 season. Where was Geoff born?

84. Len Cantello, Jimmy Cookson and Jim Cumbes between them made just short of 500 Football League appearances for the Albion. They share the same birthplace. Which city is it?

85. Albion hero Jeff Astle was born in the same part of Nottinghamshire as the famous novelist DH Lawrence, and the place shares its name with a well-known film director and actor. Where was Jeff born?

86. Five of the following six West Brom players originated in Birmingham. Who is the impostor and where was he born?
– Daryl Burgess, Jimmy Dugdale, Steve Hunt, Joleon Lescott, Graham Lovett and Craig Shakespeare.

87. Albion players David Burnside, Paul Mardon, Dick Sheppard and Cyril Williams played collectively nearly 400 Football League games for the club. Which city did they come from?

88. Four of these five West Brom players come from Glasgow. Which one hails from Edinburgh? – Eddie Colquhoun, Graham Dorrans, Jimmy Dudley, Willie Johnstone and Robert Snodgrass.

89. Between them, Albion players Don Howe, Johnny Nicholls, James Pemberton and Tommy Worton made more than 700 Football League appearances for the club. They were all born in the same town. Which one?

90. Albion players George Lee, Alex Mowatt and Stuart Naylor were born in three places in Yorkshire that sport horseracing courses. Which three?

91. Albion's first experience of football on Christmas Day itself was a chastening one. They lost 8-1 away to which Midlands club in 1896?
A. Aston Villa B. Derby County C. Nottingham Forest D. Wolves

92. It was a much warmer Yuletide feeling on Christmas Day in 1906, when the Albion didn't have to travel and beat which club 6-1?
A. Blackpool B. Clapton Orient C. Grimsby Town D. Lincoln City

93. Albion have twice left England to play on Christmas Day, and lost both times by 3-2, first in 1925 and then again in 1954. Which club beat them?

94. Which ground west of London did Baggies fans visit on successive Boxing Days in 1996 and 1997, drawing 2-2 and losing 2-1 before the club they played moved to another ground the following season?

95. Christmas Day fixtures came to an end in the 1956-57 season and West Bromwich Albion won their last one 1-0 at home to Newcastle United with a goal from which player?
A. Ray Barlow B. Frank Griffin C. Bobby Robson D. Maurice Setters

96. In the first two seasons of League football in 1888-89 and 1889-90, WBA played at home against the same Lancastrian club on consecutive Boxing Days, losing 5-0 on the first occasion before drawing 2-2 on the second. Who were their visitors?
A. Accrington B. Blackburn Rovers C. Bolton Wanders
D. Preston North End

97. Boxing Day of 1963 was very special because an incredible 66 goals were scored in the ten top-flight games that day. West Brom did their bit by sharing eight goals equally with which London club at the Hawthorns?

98. On Boxing Day of 2012, Albion won 2-1 away to QPR and the home side's goalkeeper entered into the spirit of giving to the extent of scoring one of the away side's goals. Who was that keeper?

99. Where generosity was concerned it was overflowing when Albion benefited from two own goals on Boxing Day of 1952, when they won a thriller by 5-4 on which Yorkshire ground?
A. Bramall Lane B. Elland Road C. Hillsborough D. Oakwell

100 Over Christmas in 1935, Albion won 5-2 and 5-1 at the Hawthorns against two sides beginning with M, and then, in 1957, they did it again when winning 5-3 away and 5-1 at home, this time against two team beginning with B. Which four sides' Christmases did they ruin?

You are given their league appearances, the details of their time at the club and a cryptic clue. Can you name the player in each instance?

101.   93 games – 2002-08 – Banksy was good at this.

102.   64 games – 1986-89 – Dust gatherer.

103.   71 games – 1990-92 – First to run a sub-four-minute mile.

104.   139 games – 1966-76 – Elephant man or Brummie keeper.

105.   37 games – 1950-60 – Where the president lives.

106.   44 games – 1984-86 – Popular on 14 February.

107.   285 games – 1944-59 – Midlands town associated with Duncan Edwards.

108.   97 games – 1913-22 – Posh car.

109.   109 games – 1975-79 – Free shot in golf.

110.   77 games – 1979-81 – Area of south-west London.

You are given their league appearances, the details of their time at the club and a cryptic clue. Can you name the player in each instance?

111.　85 games – 1901-05 – Found in a hospital.

112.　98 games – 1987-90 – Prime minister and compass bearing.

113.　187 games – 1979-86 – Sounds like an up-and-under in rugby.

114.　141 games – 1955-67 – Great athlete from the north-east.

115.　63 games – 1977-81 – Spent his earliest moments in bullrushes!

116.　112 games – 1990-93 – The Bard.

117.　299 games – 1975-87 – Great England fast bowler.

118.　27 games – 1929-31 – A lot of tea ended up in its harbour!

119.　168 games – 1992-97 – 1960s Scottish folk singer.

120.　113 games – 1998-2001 – Could be diamond or graphite.

13 CUP FINAL MEN PART 1: BEFORE THE ALBION

All of these players appeared in a cup final before they joined the club.

121. Which goalkeeper who played for QPR in the 1982 FA Cup final against
      Spurs joined West Brom on loan in 1987-88, ending up playing seven
      League games for the club?

122. Which Manchester City winger who scored for them in the 1976 League Cup
      final against Newcastle United signed for West Brom in 1979?

123. Which goalscorer for West Ham United against Preston North End in the
      1964 FA Cup final wound up at the Hawthorns 11 years later?

124. Which tenacious midfielder who represented Brighton & Hove Albion
      against Manchester United in the 1983 FA Cup final moved to West
      Bromwich Albion the following season?

125. Which classy midfielder had already played in FA Cup finals for both
      Aston Villa and Manchester City before his move to West Brom in 2017?

126. Which Spurs forward who took part in FA Cup finals for them in 1981 and
      1982 came to the Albion in 2017?

127. Which Albion player won the FA Cup with Manchester United in 1963 and
      Leeds United in 1972, before rocking up at the Hawthorns in 1975?

128. Which four members of Aston Villa's European Cup-winning side of 1982
      went on to play for West Bromwich Albion?

129. Which Manchester United player who appeared for them in the 1983 and
      1985 FA Cup finals joined West Brom in 1988?

130. This player could have appeared in either the 'before' or the 'after' section,
      having played for Aston Villa against Everton in the 1977 League Cup final
      before joining the Baggies in 1979 and then appearing in another League
      Cup final for Norwich City against Sunderland in 1985. Who was he?

CUP FINAL MEN PART 2: AFTER THE ALBION

All of these players appeared in a cup final after they had left the club.

131. Which ex-Albion midfielder won the FA Cup with Manchester United in 1963?

132. Which ex-Baggies striker won the FA Cup with Coventry City in 1987?

133. Which ex-West Bromwich Albion defender won the FA Cup with Liverpool in 1992?

134. Which ex-Albion player won the League Cup with Manchester City in 1976?

135. Which ex-West Brom man was a member of the Wolves side that met Spurs in the UEFA Cup final of 1972?

136. Which ex-Albion midfielder was in the Sheffield Wednesday side that played against Arsenal in both the FA Cup and League Cup finals in 1993?

137. Which ex-Baggie won the FA Cup with Manchester United in 1983, 1985 and 1990?

138. Which ex-West Bromwich Albion defender was part of the unfortunate West Ham United team that lost to Liverpool in the 2006 FA Cup final?

139. Which ex-Albion central defender was in the Aston Villa side that played Chelsea in the FA Cup final of 2000?

140. Which ex West Brom man who didn't make an appearance for them was a striker for West Ham United in the 1980 FA Cup final against Arsenal and later rejoined the Baggies from Vancouver Whitecaps in 1984, this time figuring in 54 League games and scoring 29 goals?

All of these Albion players have something to do with food. Can you identify them?

141.   43 games – 1993-95 – Culinary herb that Oscar Wilde thought was ghastly!

142.   13 games – 1961-67 – A soft toffee that can play havoc with your teeth.

143.   72 games – 1973-77 – Shortened version of up-market salad cream.

144.   42 games – 1970-72 – Maker of digestive biscuits.

145.   Three games – 1989 – Good with a curry!

146.   115 games – 1914-23 – One example of a very popular snack.

147.   21 games – 1923-30 – If you want to produce your own chips at home you need one of these.

148.   261 games – 1886-99 – Liquorice allsorts producer.

149.   53 games – 1921-24 – Part of the pig black pudding is made from.

150.   25 games – 1931-36 – Food in an uncooked state.

151. Albion have won the FA Cup five times, but in how many finals, not counting replays, have they played?

152. Who are the only club West Brom have met in an FA Cup final in both the 19th and 20th centuries?

153. Albion have never met a team from south of Birmingham in an FA Cup final – true or false?

154. Only one man has scored twice from open play in an FA Cup final for West Brom. Who is he?

155. West Bromwich Albion are one of five clubs still playing that have done something in FA Cup finals that no other clubs have done. The other four are Arsenal, Blackburn Rovers, Everton and Manchester United. What have they done?

156. Two Albion players, one in the 1888 final and the other in the 1895 final, had surnames that can also be found in England's World Cup-winning side of 1966. What were those two surnames?

157. Who is the only man to score from the penalty spot for the Albion in an FA Cup final?

158. Who are the only club that West Brom have beaten in an FA Cup final that have still not won the trophy?

159. Which two clubs beginning with the same letter are the only ones that West Bromwich Albion have played in an FA Cup final replay, the first in 1886 and the second in 1912?

160. When they lost that 1912 replay 1-0, their opponents' winning goal was scored by someone who shares a surname with a well-known England Test cricketer who was a spin bowler. What was that surname?

17 FA CUP FINALS PART 2

161. Albion have lost just one FA Cup final since the First World War. To which club, by what score and in what year?

162. Who are the only club that West Bromwich Albion have met in three FA Cup finals?

163. Which surname appeared in Albion's winning teams in both the 1892 and 1954 FA Cup finals?

164. Who was the last player to score for West Brom in an FA Cup final?

165. When Albion got back into the game at 2-2 from the penalty spot in the 1954 FA Cup final, their goalkeeper couldn't bear to watch. Who was that keeper and which Albion player was brought down to concede the penalty?

166. Who scored Albion's winning goal in the closing stages of that FA Cup final in 1954?

167. Two players who were father and son have played in goal in FA Cup finals for West Brom. The first did so in 1912, while the second appeared in both the 1931 and 1935 finals. What was their surname?

168. Who were the only three men to captain West Brom in an FA Cup final win in the 20th century?

169. Which member of Albion's winning side in 1954 came back to win the trophy again with another Midlands clubs three years later?

170. In the 1886, 1887, 1931 and 1935 FA Cup finals, West Brom had players on the field with the same surname. Which three surnames were involved?

20

171. Albion have appeared in 20 FA Cup semi-finals. Only one club have met them three times in an FA Cup semi-final. Who are they?
A. Blackburn Rovers B. Bolton Wanderers C. Everton D. Preston North End

172. The last club to play Albion in an FA Cup semi-final did so in 2008, beating them 1-0 at Wembley. Who were they and which player who later joined Albion scored their winning goal?

173. West Brom have met just two clubs from the capital in FA Cup semi-finals, losing 4-0 in 1900-01 and 1-0 in 1981-82. Who were their two opponents?

174. Who is the only player to score a hat-trick for the Baggies in an FA Cup semi-final, when his contribution was part of a 6-2 win over Nottingham Forest in a second replay in the 1891-92 season?

175. Who was the last player to score a goal for West Brom in an FA Cup semi-final, when it wasn't enough to save them from a 3-1 defeat against Ipswich Town in 1978?

176. Excluding London, which is the only city with more than one club that has provided semi-final opposition for Albion in the FA Cup?
A. Birmingham B. Liverpool C. Manchester D. Nottingham

177. Which club from Division Three North gave West Brom a big scare in the 1954 FA Cup semi-final before they went through 2-1?

178. Albion's first semi-final opponents were swept aside by 4-0 in 1885-86 and later, in the new century, became Birmingham City. What were they called in 1886?

179. Who scored both of West Brom's goals in a 2-2 semi-final draw with Aston Villa in the 1956-57 season, before Albion went down 1-0 in the replay?

180. The last two players to score in an FA Cup final and an FA Cup semi-final for Albion in the same season have surnames that begin with the same letter. Who are they?

19 FLORA, FAUNA, FISH AND FOWL

All of these Albion players relate to one of the above descriptions.
Can you identify them given their details and a clue?

181. Bird associated with Edgar Allan Poe and the Tower of London –
      259 Football League games – 1989-2000.

182. Animal traditionally the quarry in some hunting circles – 58 Football League
      games – 2000-02.

183. Bird who wrote Gulliver's Travels – 28 Football League games – 1913-20.

184. Fish that doubles as a weapon – one Football League game – 1937-46.

185. Bird and bodily function – one FA Cup tie – 1883-84.

186. Animal subject to mistreatment in Spain – four Football League games
      – 1984-86.

187. Popular game birD. 140 Football League games – 1904-10.

188. Male deer, goat, rabbit etC. 287 Football League games – 1900-03 and
      1906-14

189. Bird that doubles as a male Australian film star – 216 Football League games
      – 1925-39.

190. Where you might find some local flora and fauna – 34 Premier League
      games – 2016-21.

THE FOREIGN LEGION PART 1

Which countries did the following West Bromwich Albion players represent?

191.   Shaun Murphy – 71 Football League games for WBA. 1996-99.

192.   Jason Roberts – 89 league games for WBA. 2000-04.

193.   Nwankwo Kanu – 53 league games for WBA. 2004-06.

194.   Diomansy Kamara – 60 league games for WBA. 2005-07.

195.   Zoltán Gera – 165 league games for WBA. 2004-08 and 2011-14.

196.   Robert Koren – 126 league games for WBA. 2007-10.

197.   Do-heon Kim – 20 Premier League games for WBA. 2008-09.

198.   Chris Wood – 21 league games for WBA. 2009-13.

199.   Roman Bednár – 85 league games for WBA. 2007-12.

200.   Paul Scharner – 62 Premier League games for WBA. 2010-12.

Which countries did the following West Bromwich Albion players represent?

201.   Gonzalo Jara – 56 league games for West Bromwich Albion – 2009-13.

202.   Pablo Ibáñez – ten Premier League games for West Bromwich Albion – 2010-11.

203.   Marek Čech – 54 league games for West Bromwich Albion – 2008-11.

204.   Allan Nyom – 63 league games for West Bromwich Albion – 2016-19.

205.   Gabriel Tamas – 68 Premier League games for West Bromwich Albion – 2010-13.

206.   Goran Popov – 18 Premier League games for West Bromwich Albion – 2012-14.

207.   Saido Berahino – 105 Premier League games for West Bromwich Albion – 2010-17.

208.   Jonas Olsson – 244 league games for West Bromwich Albion – 2008-17.

209.   Nacer Chadli – 36 Premier League games for West Bromwich Albion – 2016-18.

210.   Ahmed Hegazi – 97 league games for West Bromwich Albion – 2017-21.

211. Scott Carson is unique among England internationals in gaining his four caps between 2008 and 2012 while with four different clubs. West Brom were one of them, but who were the other three?

212. Which keeper who made 19 appearances in the Football League for Albion in 1996 and 1997 won a European Cup Winners' Cup medal with another club in 1982?

213. Which West Brom keeper missed the 1954 FA Cup final after playing in all the previous rounds after an injury of such severity at Roker Park on the last day of March that he never played again?

214. Which keeper who turned out for West Brom in the Football League on 64 occasions between 1969 and 1971 also played cricket for Lancashire, Surrey, Warwickshire and Worcestershire?

215. Two Albion goalkeepers share their first names and their initials. The first played 63 times in the Football League between 1982 and 1985, while the second made just 14 appearances between 1988 and 1990. Who were they?

216. Who was a regular fixture between the posts for Albion between 1986 and 1996, performing the role on 355 occasions in league football in that period?

217. Chesterfield was a good source of top keepers in this era, and Albion got this one from that club in 1967. He went on to play for the club in exactly 250 Football League games before moving on to Shamrock Rovers in 1978. Who was he?

218. Which goalkeeper played in both of Albion's FA Cup finals of the 1890s, in 1892 and 1895?

219. Who guarded West Brom's net 267 times in the Football League between 1975 and 1986?

220. Which England international played in goal for West Bromwich Albion 209 times in the Premier League between 2011 and 2018, and which goalkeeper scored against him when he was playing for another club in 2007?

23 GOALKEEPERS PART 2

221. Which Welsh international played 40 times for Albion between 1959 and 1964, before moving on to Crystal Palace?

222. This much-travelled goalkeeper played for ten other clubs besides Albion, but was between the sticks for them in 190 league games between 2000 and 2007 – a higher figure than at any other club. Who was he?

223. Which goalkeeper, who made 34 Football League appearances for West Bromwich Albion between 1975 and 1983 before joining Leicester City, sounds as if he got bigger during his time at the Hawthorns?

224. Which Polish keeper was Albion's last line of defence in 31 league games between 2004 and 2007, and also played for their close rivals Birmingham City and Wolves?

225. Who was making his Premier League debut in goal for the Baggies when they won 3-2 against Wolves at Molineux in January 2021?

226. Why wasn't regular keeper Sam Johnstone in goal that day?

227. Which Welsh international keeper made 63 league appearances for West Brom between 2010 and 2019 after his move to the Hawthorns from Hull City?

228. Who was the first goalkeeper to play for the Albion in an FA Cup final?

229. One of the bravest keepers I've seen turned out 69 times in league football for West Brom between 2007 and 2011 and was also a Republic of Ireland international. Who was he?

230. Who is the only goalkeeper to score against West Brom in open play in a post-Second World War league game?

All of these players put through their own net to score a goal for West Bromwich Albion in the period covered.

231.   Someone who would go on to be the secretary of the FA between 1973 and 1989 scored for WBA at the Valley on 18 November 1951, when his Charlton Athletic side were beaten 3-2. Who was he?

232.   Which man who later had success as a manager in the World Cup put through his own goal to produce one of Albion's goals when they beat Spurs 3-0 on 5 September 1953?

233.   He must have liked the Albion because he gave away a penalty to put them level in the 1954 FA Cup final and then scored the game's only goal for them when they visited Deepdale on 10 September 1955 and beat Preston North End. Who was he?

234.   Which eventual World Cup winner gave West Bromwich Albion a 1-0 win over Leeds United with an own goal when they visited the Hawthorns on 12 March 1958?

235.   Another win at Deepdale came on 31 January 1959, this time by 4-2, with one of Albion's goals coming via a man who would go on to manage Manchester United. Who was he?

236.   Which ex-West Brom player did them a good turn that they barely needed on 18 September 1965 when he scored one of the goals his old club registered in their 6-2 win over his new club, Stoke City?

237.   On 26 October 1974, West Brom drew 2-2 with Millwall at the Den, with one of their goals coming from someone whose name appeared on 'Your country needs you' posters during the First World War, and who now has a stand named in his honour at their new ground. Who was he?

238.   Which ex-Leeds United hard man seeing out his career at Bristol City scored one of Albion's goals in their 2-1 win at Ashton Gate on 5 April 1977?

239.   He's managed a number of clubs and won promotion to the Premier League with Newcastle United but, on 7 November 1981, he scored for West Brom against his own club Spurs when Albion won 2-1 at White Hart Lane. Who is he?

240.   This goalkeeper was the first player to appear in all four divisions in a single season, and shares his surname with a US president. He also scored Albion's goal when they went down 3-1 at home to Tranmere Rovers on 16 April 1994. Who is he?

All of these players put through their own net to score a goal for West Bromwich Albion in the period covered.

241. Which Newcastle United forward scored for West Brom when they won 2-1 at St James' Park in a League Cup tie on 29 October 2003?

242. Which Portsmouth defender put through his own goal when Albion lost 3-2 on a visit to Fratton Park on 4 December 2004?

243. Which Manchester City defender who was no stranger to an own goal equalised for West Brom five minutes from the end when they visited their new ground on 28 December 2004?

244. When Albion drew 2-2 on a visit to Old Trafford on 16 September 2010, which Manchester United defender scored one of their goals?

245. Two months later, West Brom won 4-1 against Everton at Goodison Park, assisted on the way by a goal from which defender on the home side?

246. When WBA were beaten 3-2 at home by Manchester City on 4 December 2013, one of the Albion goals came courtesy of the visiting keeper. Who was he?

247. Which Argentinian Leicester City player put through his own net to score the game's only goal when West Brom won away on 1 November 2014?

248. Which West Ham United defender scored for Albion in a 3-3 draw at the Hawthorns on 12 February 2011 and then extended similar generosity in a 1-1 draw at Upton Park on 29 November 2015?

249. Which Manchester City defender got Albion's goal in a 1-1 draw at the Etihad on 15 December 2020?

250. Who scored against his own side when Albion drew 2-2 with Aston Villa at Villa Park on 25 April 2021?

251.   It depends on which source you read where West Brom's early grounds are concerned, but Cooper's Hill and Dartmouth both get a mention in the late 1870s before a move to Bunn's Field in Walsall Street in 1881. Just like the Hawthorns later on, the ground was named for trees. What was it called? A. The Birches B. The Cedars C. The Elms D. The Oaks

252.   That ground was something of a stopgap arrangement and the following year the club upped sticks when Dartmouth Cricket Club offered to hire out their ground to the Albion. The ground was a measurement of area. What was it called? A. Two Acres B. Four Acres C. Six Acres D. Eight Acres

253.   In 1885 Albion made the short move to land near Sandwell Brewery. Known as Stoney Lane, the new ground boasted a stand for 600 spectators and was immediately known by what nickname by Albion's growing number of fans?

254.   The new century brought a new ground (one the club have played on ever since), with much hard effort making it capable of holding 30,000 a few months after it was secured. It was situated on the Birmingham Road on land called the Hawthorns Estate due to American hawthorn bushes being used to partition fields in that area. The club's secretary therefore suggested 'the Hawthorns' as an appropriate name. His name must have suggested how everyone felt about being in their new ground! Who was he?

255.   Which Midlands club were West Brom's first visitors to the new ground on 3 September 1900, in a game that finished 1-1?
       A. Aston Villa B. Derby County C. Notts County D. Wolves

256.   The first Albion player to score at the Hawthorns saved the home side a point when he equalised ten minutes from the end. Who was he?
       A. Abe Jones B. Tom Perry C. 'Chippy' Simmons D. Jim Stevenson

257.   As could be gathered from the previous question, unfortunately it wasn't an Albion player who scored the first goal at the Hawthorns. However, it was a legendary player who won 23 international caps when they weren't given out like dolly mixtures, and someone whose statue stands near the dugout of his club's ground, unless of course it has been moved for an inappropriate thought he had in 1895! Who was he?

258.   The Hawthorns was selected as a venue for an England international on three occasions – in 1922, 1924 and 1945. The first and last of them were against Ireland and Wales respectively, but the middle one saw a 4-0 England win over which country?
       A. Austria B. Belgium C. France D. Hungary

259.   Which club were West Brom playing when they set the record attendance of 64,815 at the Hawthorns in a 3-1 FA Cup quarter-final win on 6 March 1937?
       A. Arsenal B. Huddersfield Town C. Manchester City D. Preston North End

260.   Who are the only club to figure twice in the list of the largest ten Hawthorns crowds?

INTERNATIONALS: ENGLAND (POST-WW2)

27

261. Which full back's 23 caps while at Albion between 1958 and 1960 is still the highest number of post-Second World War caps for England by any Albion player?

262. Which player who won his first England cap while at West Brom went on to gain 90 of them?

263. Which two players whose surnames begin with the same letter both received just one England cap while at the Albion, the first player in 1955 and the second in 1971?

264. Ronnie Allen and Jeff Astle are two of the biggest names in the history of West Bromwich Albion, and they earned the same number of England caps. How many?

265. Which West Bromwich Albion player had a 50 per cent scoring rate for England when his two games for his country in 1954 produced a goal in a 4-2 win against Scotland at Hampden Park?

266. Who won all of his 20 England caps with West Brom between 1958 and 1962?

267. Which West Bromwich Albion player scored eight goals in his 14 appearances for his country and was their top scorer in the 1958 World Cup in Sweden?

268. With which club did Laurie Cunningham win the most England caps: West Brom or Real Madrid?

269. Steve Hunt and Derek Statham won five caps between them while at the Albion in the 1980s. Who shaded it 3-2?

270. Cyrille Regis played four times as many games for England while at West Brom as he did at Coventry City – true or false?

271. In the late 1940s and early 1950s it wasn't unknown for someone to play for both Northern Ireland and the Republic. Which member of the Throstles' FA Cup-winning side of 1954 was capped for both?

272. Which centre forward was another who played for both when he was involved in nine games for Northern Ireland and 14 for the Republic, his Albion career comprising 165 Football League games between 1946 and 1950?

273. To complete a trio of players who achieved this 'double', which centre half came to Albion from Belfast Celtic in 1946, making 190 appearances in League football for the club until 1951, and on the way turned out 17 times for Northern Ireland after an initial couple of caps for the Republic?

274. This front man played just eight times for West Brom in the Football League in 1985, but in one of his 65 appearances for his country he famously scored a goal that beat the hosts, Spain, in the 1982 World Cup. Who was he?

275. Which midfielder who played in 14 Football League games for West Bromwich Albion in 1969, before his move to Wolves, was capped seven times by Northern Ireland?

276. Which player who performed many roles in his 382 league games for the Baggies between 2007 and 2020 was also capped 65 times for Northern Ireland?

277. Which central defender who turned out for the Albion in 89 Premier League games between 2015 and 2018 earned 93 caps for his country from 2006 onwards?

278. This defensive midfielder who played in 19 Premier League games for the club in 2014 and 2015 received a total of 79 caps for Northern Ireland between 2003 and 2016. Who was he?

279. This defender ran out 203 times in Premier League matches for West Brom between 2011 and 2018, and also amassed a career total of 80 caps for Northern Ireland. Who was he?

280. This forward who made exactly 50 appearances for Northern Ireland was at West Bromwich Albion between 1998 and 2002, making 114 league appearances for them. Who was he?

29 INTERNATIONALS: REP OF IRELAND (POST-WW2)

281. Which midfielder who made 35 appearances for the Republic between 2008 and 2012 was capped during his 14 games at West Brom after joining the club from Blackburn Rovers, before moving on to Bolton Wanderers?

282. Which midfielder received ten of his 45 caps for the Republic while making 65 appearances for the Baggies between 1984 and 1986?

283. Which forward had two spells at the Albion, one in the 1960s and other in the 1970s, playing 26 Football League games along the way and being capped 42 times for his country?

284. Which defender received 33 caps for the Republic between 2006 and 2016, and played 32 times in the Football League for West Brom between 2006 and 2007?

285. Which winger who played in 106 Football League games for Albion between 1997 and 1999 ended up with an even higher total of caps for the Republic of Ireland?

286. Which brilliant midfielder earned seven of his 59 caps for the Republic while at West Brom near the end of his career, appearing for them in 75 Football League games between 1975 and 1977?

287. Which forward played in 65 league games for West Bromwich Albion between 2009 and 2012 before joining Nottingham Forest, and ended his career with 30 caps for his country?

288. Which front man who was at the Albion from 2011 to 2014 played in 81 Premier League games for the club and finished his international career with 88 caps?

289. Which controversial character ended up one short of 100 Premier League appearances on the left wing for Albion between 2015 and 2018 while clocking up an impressive number of Republic of Ireland caps?

290. He gained exactly 50 caps as a defender between 1969 and 1980, 16 of which came while he was at West Bromwich Albion between 1975 and 1979. Who was he?

INTERNATIONALS: SCOTLAND (POST-WW2) 30

291. Which combative Albion midfielder was capped twice for Scotland in the late 1960s?

292. At the same time, another West Brom player who was, in the parlance of the day, the club's principal schemer, picked up two Scottish caps. Who was he?

293. Which hugely talented but wayward Albion winger received 13 of his 21 Scottish caps while at the club between 1976 and 1978?

294. Which forward who was at the Hawthorns between 2001 and 2004 received all six of his caps for Scotland in 2002?

295. Which Albion midfielder who played 29 league games for them between 2006 and 2007 gained an overall total of 14 caps for Scotland between 2004 and 2007?

296. Which creative Albion player won six of his total of 50 Scottish caps while in the Black Country between 1971 and 1972?

297. Which wholehearted midfielder won 80 Scottish caps between 2004 and 2018 while with Manchester United and West Brom?

298. Another midfielder who played 166 league games for Albion between 2008 and 2015 received 12 Scottish caps while with West Brom and Norwich City. Who was he?

299. Yet another midfielder who was at the Hawthorns between 2000 and 2003, making 88 league appearances for the club, gained two Scottish caps in that time. Who was he?

300. Let's complete this glut of midfielders with someone who played 309 league games for the Albion between 2007 and 2019 and was capped 46 times for his country. Who was he?

301. Which defender who played in 139 Football League games for the Throstles between 1993 and 2001 made his sole appearance for Wales in 1996?

302. This stalwart full back appeared in 314 Football League games for West Brom and was capped 26 times for his country between 1960 and 1969. Who was he?

303. Which midfielder made 131 league appearances for the Albion between 2001 and 2006 and received 15 caps while at the Hawthorns and Nottingham Forest?

304. Which striker was capped 59 times for Wales while at five clubs between 2002 and 2013, and had 43 league outings for West Bromwich Albion between 2004 and 2006?

305. Which midfielder made 123 league appearances for West Brom between 2002 and 2007 and turned out 34 times for Wales between 2001 and 2009, leaving the Hawthorns under a cloud after falling out with manager Bobby Robson?

306. Which lively, volatile character was capped 51 times for Wales while with seven clubs between 1977 and 1986, the last two of them coming when he was with West Brom?

307. Someone else who got two caps while at the Albion was a winger who ended up with 39 of them. He played 34 Football League games for West Brom at the back end of the 1960s. Who was he?

308. Which full back received 33 of his 43 caps for Wales while at West Bromwich Albion and the other ten while at Southampton, with all of them coming between 1954 and 1966?

309. He doesn't sound Welsh but he got eight caps for that country, six of them coming while he was at Huddersfield Town and the other two while playing for West Brom, where he appeared in 51 Football League games between 1962 and 1970. Who was this member of the forward line?

310. Which central defender was capped 35 times for Wales while at three clubs between 2014 and 2019, his time at the Albion consisting of 13 Premier League games in 2015-16?

311. The only time that West Bromwich Albion won the League Cup was in 1966, on the last occasion the final was held over two legs, when they won the second leg 4-1 at the Hawthorns after trailing 2-1 after the away leg. Whom did they beat 5-3 on aggregate?

312. Albion were also in the inaugural one-off final at Wembley the following season, when a 2-0 half-time lead was squandered against a Third Division side, Albion going down 3-2 to which club?

313. The scorer of the winning goal against West Bromwich Albion that afternoon was appropriate as his side had come back from the dead. Who was he?

314. West Brom were involved in their third final in five seasons in the competition in 1970, when once again they took the lead before losing in extra time — to which club?

315. In the four matches involved in those three League Cup finals, who was the only West Bromwich Albion player to score twice in a game?

316. The same player scored the Albion's first and last of the eight goals they scored in those three finals. Who was he?

317. The Baggies' opponents in the 1966 final included a player who later turned out ten times in an Albion shirt. Who was he?

318. Which member of the Albion side that contested the 1970 League Cup later went on to play for the club that beat them that day?

319. Which two managers were in charge of the Throstles in those three finals?

320. How many more people attended Albion's second Wembley final in 1970 than were at the first one in 1967?
A. 11 B. 111 C. 1,111 D. 11,111

321.   Which two men who share the same surname managed
        West Bromwich Albion, the first for six games in 1991 and the second
        for four games in 2006?

322.   Which two Albion managers have also managed England?

323.   What have Frank Heaven and Brian Little done that no other West Brom
        managers have?

324.   Which legendary figure managed the club for over 46 years and is the only
        man to take the Albion to a Football League title during his time in charge?

325.   Which four West Brom managers have scored a goal in a post-Second
        World War FA Cup final?

326.   Which man who had charge of West Brom for one game in February 2011
        holds a unique and unwanted record as a manager in having been knocked
        out of the FA Cup with three different clubs in the same season, those clubs
        being Portsmouth, Blackpool and Blackburn Rovers?

327.   Which two West Brom managers won World Cup winners' medals as
        players?

328.   Which Albion manager from the 1990s had scored for Arsenal in a League
        Cup final in the 1960s?

329.   If you take the first name of Albion's second manager and place it in front
        of the surname of their first manager, you produce a very famous American
        manufacturer. Who?

330.   Who is the only West Brom manager to manage a club that won the
        Champions League with him in charge?

331. Which four Scots have managed West Bromwich Albion in more than 20 post-Second World War league games?

332. Which Albion manager took another club to the Football League title in the 1980s?

333. Which two West Brom managers won the FA Cup as managers with other clubs in the 1980s?

334. Which progressive manager took Albion to within an ace of the first Football League and FA Cup double of the 20th century in 1954?

335. Who is the only Spaniard to have managed West Brom?

336. Who is the only manager to have come top of any division with West Brom since 1920?

337. Among managers in charge of the club in all competitions who have been in control in more than 20 games, Sam Allardyce won 15.4 per cent of his games and Alan Pardew won 14.3 per cent, but which manager, on 14.29 per cent, just shades the award for the worst recorD. one that was created in the mid-1980s?

338. At the other end of the scale, among managers in charge for more than 20 games this century, who, with a 47.92 per cent win rate, has the best record?

339. Who is the only manager to have led West Brom to victory in a play-off final?

340. Which post-Second World War Albion manager needs just one letter inserted into his name to become the leading character in Herman Melville's Moby-Dick?

341. When Albion won the Football League in the first season after the First World War, they opened their campaign with a 3-1 home win on 30 August 1919 against a club from Lancashire. Which one?
A. Bolton Wanderers B. Burnley C. Oldham Athletic D. Preston North End

342. On 7 August 1999, Albion drew 1-1 at home in their last opening league game of the 20th century, while on 12 August 2000 they lost 1-0 away in their first opening-day fixture of the 21st century. The names of their opponents share their first two letters. Who were they?

343. West Brom beat Manchester United on the opening day of the 1959-60 season, winning 3-2 at the Hawthorns. Then, five years later, this time away from home, they ran into Manchester United again first time up, drawing 2-2 on 22 August 1964. One Manchester United defender was unfortunate enough to score an own goal in both games. Who was he?
A. Shay Brennan B. Noel Cantwell C. Tony Dunne D. Bill Foulkes

344. Who are the only club that West Bromwich Albion have met three years in a row on the opening day of the season – in 1904, 1905 and 1906?

345. Albion's opponents on the opening day of 1938-39 – the last season before the Second World War – and their opponents on the opening day of the first season back after the war, in 1946-47, were both Towns who played in white shirts. Who were they?

346. Albion travelled to the capital for the first time on the opening day of a season on 29 August 1931, and came away with a 1-0 win over which club?
A. Arsenal B. Chelsea C. Spurs D. West Ham United

347. Which Yorkshire club beat West Brom on the opening day of successive seasons, in 1960-61 and 1961-62, without conceding a goal?
A. Huddersfield Town B. Leeds United C. Sheffield United D. Sheffield Wednesday

348. On 23 August 1952, Albion won a seven-goal thriller in London by 4-3 against the club that had won the Football League title in April of that same year. Who were they?

349. After experiencing relegation from the Premier League in 2005-06, Albion started life at the second level of English football on 5 August 2006 with a 2-0 win at the Hawthorns. Their new centre forward bagged both goals and shared their first letter of his name with the first letter of the club he helped to beat. Who was he and who were they?

350. Against which club who later left the Football League did Albion open the 1901-02 season on 2 September 1901?
A. Bradford Park Avenue B. Burton United C. Gainsborough Town
D. Glossop

351. Let's at least start with something that holds some value. In which competition did Albion lose 7-1 on aggregate to Manchester United in the two-legged final of 1955 and 6-3 to Sunderland in 1969, before winning it 5-0 against Wolves in 1976?

352. Which two London clubs did Albion meet in the Charity Shield in the interwar years?

353. West Brom's last goal in that competition was a consolation when they were hammered 6-1 by Manchester City at Maine Road on 3 August 1968. Who scored it?
A. Jeff Astle B. Tony Brown C. Asa Hartford D. Dick Krzywicki

354. Which European club visited the Hawthorns to celebrate Albion's centenary on 11 August 1979, in a game the home side won 1-0?

355. Albion entered two competitions in the 1970s, the first sponsored b an oil company in which they didn't trouble the judges, and the second, sponsored by a brewery in which, after wins against Wrexham and Halifax Town, they lost on penalties to Colchester United after a 4-4 draw at the Hawthorns in the final. What were the two competitions called?

356. In the early 1990s the Albion played against Shrewsbury Town, Lincoln City, Exeter City, Walsall, Mansfield Town, Torquay United and Stoke City over a couple of seasons in what competition?

357. Between 1985 and 1990 West Brom were involved in a competition that, by the time it was quietly euthanised, had had three different names. They came up against Brighton, Crystal Palace and Chelsea in 1985-86 and Millwall in 1986-87 in its first incarnation, then met Oldham Athletic and Ipswich Town under its first alias in in 1987-88 and West Ham United in 1988-89. Finally, under the competition's third name, they lost 5-0 to Derby County and 5-3 to Barnsley. What were the competition's three names?

358. West Brom entered the Anglo-Scottish Cup in 1975-76 and 1976-77 while seeing neither hide nor hair of any club from north of the border! When it became the Tennent-Caledonian Cup the following season, Albion won it after two wins at Ibrox Park, by 4-3 in the semi-final and 2-0 in the final. Which two Scottish clubs did they beat?

359. In the season after that, West Brom lost a third-place match, always an absurdity, to Hearts after losing in the semi-final on penalties following a 1-1 draw – to which English club?
A. Birmingham City B. Coventry City C. Leicester City D. Southampton

360. 1 Albion played in the Anglo-Italian Cup for two seasons in the early 1970s, wisely gave it a miss in the 1980s and then had two more goes at it in the 1990s. When they travelled on 16 May 1970 to play Lanerossi Vicenza, the score stood at 1-1 after 76 minutes when the match was abandoned. Why?

361. In their first experience of a penalty shoot-out in a major competition, in the League Cup of 2001-02, West Brom won through 4-3 after a 1-1 away draw against which club?

362. In the FA Cup Cup fifth round of 2006-07, the Baggies experienced the other side of this unsatisfactory way of deciding the outcome when they lost a shoot-out by 5-4 after a 1-1 draw at the Hawthorns in a replay against which northern club?

363. In the following season they won the shoot-out 4-3 against a London club after an FA Cup third-round replay at the Hawthorns had ended in a 2-2 draw. Which club went out of the competition?

364. In 2013-14 it was another London club who turned the tables on West Bromwich Albion when they won a League Cup third-round tie 4-3 on penalties after a 1-1 draw at the Hawthorns. Who were they?

365. The following season, in the second round of the same competition, Albion won 7-6 on penalties after a 1-1 home draw against a club who were successful in the competition in 1986. Who were they?

366. In the 2015-16 season, Albion were successful via this method in both domestic cup competitions. In the fourth round of the FA Cup, after a 1-1 away draw in a replay necessitated by an earlier 2-2 draw at the Hawthorns, they came through 4-3 on penalties against a club known half a century earlier for the odd bit of giantkilling. Who were they?

367. Which club, whose name begins with the same letter as the previous answer, did Albion eliminate from the League Cup in 2015-16 by 5-3 on penalties after a 0-0 draw at the Hawthorns?

368. That same League Cup competition produced another penalty shoot-out the following season, after a 2-2 away draw. This time Albion weren't so lucky, going down 4-3 on penalties – to which club?

369. The 2020-21 season was a bad one for West Brom where penalty shoot-outs were concerned: they went out of both cup competitions by that method. In the FA Cup third round they lost 3-2 on penalties after a 2-2 draw at the Hawthorns against opposition from Lancashire. Who were they?

370. In the League Cup of that same season, the Albion lost 5-4 on penalties to a London club, also after a 2-2 draw at the Hawthorns. Which club progressed to the next round?

The Football League play-offs were introduced in 1986-87 and Albion had their first experience of them in 1992-93 as they made their way out of the third tier of English football.

371. Which Welsh club did they beat 3-2 on aggregate in the semi-final to reach the Wembley final?

372. A crowd of 53,471 turned up to see West Brom win 3-0 in that 1993 play-off final – against which club?

373. Who was the only Albion man to score in both the 1993 semi-final and the final?

374. In 2000-01 the play-offs provided an opportunity for West Bromwich Albion to get into the Premier League, but they didn't get past the semi-final stage, losing 5-2 on aggregate to which Lancastrians?

375. Albion got another stab at it in the 2006-07 season, winning their semi-final 4-2 on aggregate against which Midlands club?

376. However, big disappointment was in store for them in the first play-off final at the new Wembley when they were beaten 1-0 – by which club?

377. Which ex-Baggie lined up against them on that day at Wembley, playing in the opposition's forward line?

378. Albion sported four players with surnames starting with K that day. Who were they?

379. If 2006-07 was hard to take, West Brom's only experience of the play-offs since then was even more painful. The details are elsewhere in the quiz, but in what season did they have unfulfilled hopes of Premier League football?

380. Who is the only player to have scored a total of three goals in the play-offs for West Brom?

POT LUCK

381.   Two strikers who between them gained 27 England caps had short and contrasting experiences at the Hawthorns. The first one played just four Football League games in the mid-1980s, while the second had three outings in an Albion shirt on loan in 1992. Who were the two players?

382.   On which London ground did West Brom lose 6-1 in the Premier League but win 3-2 in the League Cup in the 2005-06 season?

383.   Two West Bromwich Albion favourites – Clive Clark and Len Cantello – ended their Albion careers with exactly the same number of Football League appearances. What was that number?
A. 201 B. 251 C. 301 D. 351

384.   When Albion met Italian club Bologna in Europe in 1966-67, one of their opponents had scored in the 1966 World Cup final, and the phenomenon repeated itself when they met Spanish outfit Valencia in 1978-79, this player having scored in the 1978 World Cup final. Who were the two players?

385.   What was West Bromwich Albion's first name when they arrived on the scene in 1878, and why were they so called?

386.   Which Albion player who went on to become England's manager played for the club exactly the same number of times as the number of games he managed England?

387.   Which player who shares his name with a football club scored Birmingham's goal against Albion in the 1931 FA Cup final and enjoyed playing at the Hawthorns when he scored twice there in an England international in 1924?

388.   Who became the only Albion player to score six times in a Football League game when he grabbed all of their goals in a 6-3 win over Blackpool at the Hawthorns on 17 September 1927?

389.   West Brom's first six-figure buy came from Sunderland in 1969 and their first seven-figure purchase arrived via Preston North End in 1997. Who were the two players?

390.   On 19 May 1888, West Brom, as holders of the FA Cup, travelled to Glasgow to meet the Scottish Cup holders in a match billed, with some hyperbole, as 'the championship of the world'! Conditions were almost unplayable and few spectators in the vast open bowl of Hampden Park escaped being drowned rats! Unofficially, Albion lost 4-1 to a club that shared its name with a character, rather appropriately, in Trainspotting. Who were they?

RED CARDS

391. Which West Brom player was sent off after 63 minutes of his very first Premier League game at Old Trafford on 17 August 2002?

392. Ahmed Hegazi was sent off in a 2-0 away defeat on 6 April 2019, and repeated the feat after scoring in a 4-2 win at the Hawthorns on 5 July 2020. The nicknames of the two opposition clubs complement each other. Who were they?

393. Which Albion player was shown a red card against Burnley 12 minutes after scoring the only goal of the game at Turf Moor on 19 August 2017?

394. Which West Brom player was sent off twice in Lancashire, at Wigan Athletic and Blackburn Rovers, in the 2018-19 season?

395. Semi Ajayi received a red card when Albion won 1-0 away in London on 25 January 2020, and then got another in a 0-0 away draw in Lancashire on 20 February 2021. Albion's two opponents share the same colours. Who were they?

396. West Brom lost 2-1 against Blackpool at Bloomfield Road on 1 November 2010 after playing with nine men for the last hour of the game. Which two of their players saw red?

397. Which Albion player went for an early bath after 63 minutes of their 1-1 home draw with Sheffield Wednesday on 29 December 2018?

398. Jason Roberts in 2003, Youssouf Mulumbu in 2010 and Gareth McAuley in 2015 were all sent off against the same club. Which one?

399. After scoring in the sixth minute for West Brom in their 3-0 away win at Southampton on 27 April 2013, which Albion player fell foul of the referee with 20 minutes remaining?

400. Three London clubs were involved in three West Bromwich Albion dismissals three years running. First, an Albion player went in the 38th minute of a 3-0 defeat at Fulham in 2012; another player went early when Spurs won 1-0 at the Hawthorns in 2013; finally, in 2014, another West Brom man was sent off after half an hour in a 2-0 defeat at the hands of Chelsea at Stamford Bridge. Who were the three players?

Here is a list of ten West Bromwich Albion players from this period.
Can you match the player with his details below in each case?

401.   Alf Bentley

402.   Bobby Blood

403.   Jimmy Cookson

404.   Stan Davies

405.   Ben Garfield

406.   Billy Garraty

407.   Billy Light

408.   Jack Mahon

409.   Teddy Pheasant

410.   Walter Robbins

1.   122 games – from Chesterfield 1927 – to Plymouth Argyle 1933

2.   109 games – from Burton Wanderers 1896 – to Brighton & Hove Albion 1902

3.   28 games – from Southampton 1936 – to Colchester United 1938

4.   53 games – from Port Vale 1921 – to Stockport County 1924

5.   140 games – from Wolves 1904 – to Leicester Fosse 1910

6.   84 games – from Cardiff City 1932 – to Newport County 1939

7.   113 games – from Leeds United 1935 – to Huddersfield Town 1938

8.   53 games – from Leicester Fosse 1908 – to Lincoln City 1910

9.   97 games – from Bolton Wanderers 1913 – to Burton Albion 1922

10.   147 games – from Everton 1921 – to Birmingham 1927

411. Which left winger joined West Bromwich Albion from one 'blue' city in Leicester in 1958 and, after 81 Football League games, left for another 'blue' city in Cardiff?

412. Which Albion keeper made 217 Football League appearances for the club after his arrival from Crystal Palace in 1958, before joining Portsmouth in 1967?

413. Which forward turned out for West Brom in 262 Football League games after joining them from Bradford Park Avenue in 1953, before a move to Chelsea a decade later?

414. Which tough-tackling midfielder arrived at the Hawthorns from Exeter City in 1955, before leaving for Manchester United in 1960 after 120 Football League outings?

415. Which ball-playing inside forward came from Bristol City in 1955, made 127 Football League appearances in an Albion shirt and then departed for Southampton in 1962?

416. Which right winger who scored one of the most important goals in the club's history came from Shrewsbury Town in 1951 and left for Northampton Town in 1959, clocking up 240 Football League games on the way?

417. The left winger who regularly partnered the right winger of the previous question joined the Albion from Nottingham Forest in 1949 and retired after great service and a total of 271 Football League appearances. Who was he?

418. Which full back played a total of 189 Football League games for West Brom after signing from Middlesbrough in 1950, before trying his luck with non-League Poole Town in 1955?

419. Which Welsh defender came from Wrexham in 1950, racked up 226 Football League games and then went south to Southampton in 1962?

420. Which goalkeeper played 327 times in the Football League for Albion after leaving Charlton Athletic in 1945, and before a move to Coventry City in 1958?

421.   Which previous Football League title winner joined Albion from Wolves in 1965 but, after 14 League games for the Baggies, went back in 1966 to Ipswich Town, the club with which he had won the League in 1962?

422.   Which forward signed by West Brom from Sunderland in 1969 went on to play 128 Football League games for the club before his move to Norwich City in 1973?

423.   Which midfielder came from Scunthorpe United in 1963 and left to join Hull City in 1971 after contributing 284 Football League games to Albion's cause?

424.   Which Burnley forward became a Baggie in 1962 and then, 59 Football League matches later, went down the road to St Andrew's in 1965?

425.   Which Albion winger started out at QPR, became a Throstle in 1961 and, more than 300 Football League games later, went back to where he started?

426.   Which West Brom forward came from Leicester City in 1972 and moved on to Crystal Palace in 1983 after an impressive 279 Football League outings for the club?

427.   Which Albion forward who made 92 appearances for the Baggies left QPR to join them in 1969, before returning to the Smoke with Orient in 1977?

428.   Which West Brom central defender who turned out for the club 46 times in League football came to the Hawthorns from Bury in 1967 and left for Sheffield United in 1968?

429.   Which Durham-born midfielder started out at the Albion from schoolboy football in 1962, leaving for Ipswich Town in 1969 after a total of 69 Football League appearances?

430.   Which centre half played 144 Football League games for West Bromwich Albion between 1966 and 1971 after a fine career at Burnley? He had a spell with Belgian club KV Mechelen after leaving the Midlands.

431. Which defender played in 172 Football League games for Albion before his retirement, after joining the club from Cambridge United in 1978?

432. Which centre forward played 91 times in the Football League for West Brom after signing from Coventry City in 1983, before his move to Sheffield Wednesday in 1985?

433. Which midfielder managed 65 Football League games for West Bromwich Albion after joining from Brighton & Hove Albion in 1984, moving on to Manchester City in 1986?

434. Which forward played in 114 Football League games for West Bromwich Albion after his move from Stoke City in 1988, ending up at Grimsby Town in 1991?

435. Which forward arrived at the Hawthorns from Middlesbrough in 1979 and moved on to Sheffield Wednesday in 1983, in the interim making 59 Football League appearances for the Albion?

436. Which forward joined Albion from Spurs in 1985 before moving back to the capital with Charlton Athletic in 1987 after 39 Football League games?

437. Which forward left West Bromwich Albion for Manchester City in 1986 after playing 32 times in the Football League for West Brom following a move from Sheffield Wednesday the previous year?

438. An easy one! Who made 86 Football League appearances for the Albion after signing from Orient in 1977, before getting his dream move to Real Madrid in 1979?

439. Which central defender moved to Darlington in 1989 after 64 Football League games for the Baggies, having joined the club from Stoke City in 1986?

440. Which midfielder who scored in the 1981 FA Cup final replay for Manchester City against Spurs left to go to the Hawthorns soon after, going on to play 156 times in League football for West Brom before a move to Charlton Athletic in 1987?

441. Which winger made 106 Football League appearances for West Brom, signing from Preston North End in 1997 and leaving for the differently coloured stripes of Sunderland in 1999?

442. Which Albion defender who played 113 times in the Football League for the club arrived at the Hawthorns in 1998 from Derby County and moved on to Walsall in 2001?

443. Which midfielder arrived from Grimsby Town in 1995, turned out for the Albion on 39 occasions in the Football League and then joined Swansea City in 1997?

444. Which midfielder joined West Bromwich Albion from Sheffield Wednesday in 1990, clocking up 112 Football League games before leaving for Grimsby Town in 1993?

445. Which forward joined West Brom from Arsenal in 1991 and was one Football League outing short of 50 when he decamped to Swansea City in 1994?

446. Which midfielder ran up a total of 240 Football League appearances between his arrival from Scunthorpe United in 1992 and his departure for Sheffield United in 1998?

447. Which Albion defender appeared 103 times in the Football League for the club after joining from Everton in 1996, before leaving for Torquay United in 1999?

448. Which midfielder played in 60 Football League games for West Bromwich Albion after arriving at the Hawthorns from Notts County in 1996, eventually joining Halifax Town two years later?

449. Which Albion midfielder joined the club from Huddersfield Town in 1992 and made 168 Football League appearances before his move to Grimsby Town in 1997?

450. Which West Brom midfield man arrived at the club from Derby County in 1997 and left for Tranmere Rovers in 2000, having made 109 Football League appearances for the Baggies in the interim?

451. Which central defender played in 65 Premier and Football League games for the Baggies after joining the club from Luton Town in 2005, eventually leaving for Aston Villa in 2008?

452. Which midfielder racked up 196 Premier and Football League games for the Albion after his arrival from Middlesbrough in 2004, before departing for Fulham in 2010?

453. Another midfielder made 91 Premier League appearances for West Brom after joining the club from Manchester United in 2015, and then moved on to play for Stoke City in 2017. Who was he?

454. Which goalkeeper, who had a season on loan at Birmingham City not long after arriving at the Albion from Hull City in 2010, made 63 Premier League appearances before retiring from the game?

455. Which central defender arrived at the Hawthorns from Rochdale in 2010 and was just six games short of 200 in the Premier and Football Leagues for the Baggies when he moved to Watford in 2019?

456. Which midfielder played 92 Premier League games for West Bromwich Albion after his transfer from Blackburn Rovers in 2010, before a move back to Lancashire to play for their arch-rivals Burnley in 2014?

457. Which central defender arrived at the club from Bolton Wanderers in 2008 and then, in 2011, went on to try his luck in French football with Dijon after making 48 Football and Premier League appearances for Albion?

458. Which forward made 81 Premier League appearances for West Brom after joining the club from Reading in 2011, finally departing for Hull City in 2014?

459. This is a story of three Ws. He came from Wigan Athletic to play up front for the Albion in 2005 and moved on to Watford in 2007 after 68 Premier and Football League outings. Who was he?

460. Which player's 44 Premier and Football League matches for the Albion came between spells at Burnley and Preston North End, joining West Brom from the former in 2005 and leaving for the latter in 2008?

461.   This delightful, classy front man was also a ruthless goalscorer, ending up with just over a goal every two games by scoring 208 times in 415 Albion Football League games. He played for two other clubs, one before West Brom and one after. Who are the two clubs, one from the Midlands and one from London, and for which of those clubs did he score the most League goals?

462.   Debuts just don't come better than this. A Hawthorns crowd of 60,945 (those were the days) and a goal in a 1-1 draw with the old enemy on 4 March 1950. Whom did the Albion play?

463.   How many times in the 1950s, the decade that seemed to belong to Allen, was he West Brom's leading League goalscorer?

464.   Although Allen won just five England caps, the two matches in which he scored were two memorable victories – by 4-2 away in April 1954 and 3-1 at Wembley in December 1954. Which two countries were defeated?

465.   Ronnie Allen scored League hat-tricks against eight different clubs. They were Bolton Wanderers, Wolves, Huddersfield Town, Chelsea, Cardiff City, Newcastle United, Birmingham City and Manchester City. Against which one of the eight did he score four times in a 6-1 win at the Hawthorns on 21 November 1953?

466.   Which one of the eight clubs was the only one against whom he scored hat-tricks in both the Football League and the FA Cup?

467.   In which season were Allen's 27 League goals the best record of any player in Division One?

468.   Ronnie Allen would have been well pleased with his hat-trick against Wolves at Molineux on 29 September 1954, but the game wasn't in the League or the FA Cup. What were the clubs playing for and how did the game end up?

469.   On 12 May 1951, Albion lost 4-3 at home to SC Wacker of Austria despite two goals from Allen. Three days later, Albion beat Floriana of Malta 2-0. The two matches were part of the celebrations of which event?

470.   The last two goals Ronnie Allen scored in his superb career at the Hawthorns came in home and away wins over the same club from Lancashire. Albion won 1-0 away in October 1960 and 3-2 at home in February 1961 – against which club?
A. Blackburn Rovers B. Blackpool C. Bolton Wanderers D. Burnley

12 TOP THROSTLES NO 2: JEFF ASTLE

471. 'The king of the Hawthorns' came from one Midlands club for £25,000 after scoring 32 goals for them in 103 Football League games, and made his Albion debut against another Midlands club on 30 September 1964. Who were the two clubs?

472. Jeff Astle was Albion's top League goalscorer four times, but he had to share the honours with another player in 1965-66. Who also had a total of 18 that season?

473. Astle is known for his feat of scoring in every round when the Baggies won the FA Cup in 1968. The last player before him to achieve it scored the last of his goals against Albion in the 1954 FA Cup final, while only one player has managed it since 1968. Who are the two men standing either side of Jeff Astle here?

474. There's a neat symmetry to Jeff Astle's five England caps. The first two were at Wembley, while the last two were at Guadalajara. The middle one, the only match to finish in a draw, was on which ground?
A. Dalymount Park B. Hampden Park C. Ninian Park D. Windsor Park

475. In which season was Jeff Astle the top scorer in Division One with 25 goals to his name?

476. It didn't take long for Astle to endear himself to the Albion fans: his first goals, which came in a 5-1 win at the Hawthorns on 10 October 1964, were against which club?

477. Astle scored 14 FA Cup goals and 19 League Cup goals for the Baggies, his two hat-tricks in cup games coming in the latter competition. They came in home wins of 6-1 and 4-0 in 1965-66 and 1966-67. Against which two clubs?

478. Five of his six League hat-tricks came at the Hawthorns, the only one on an opponents' ground coming in a 4-3 win on 10 September 1965 against a club that were spending the only season in their history in the top flight. Who were they?

479. Which city's two clubs both suffered a Jeff Astle hat-trick, both coming in September – the first in a 4-2 win in 1965 and the second in a 4-1 win in 1967?
A. Birmingham B. Manchester C. Nottingham D. Sheffield

480. Against which club did Jeff Astle score his last Albion goal in a 2-2 home draw on 23 February 1974, and to which country did he move after his West Brom career ended?

481. With a name suited to a character in a comic and an ability to wreck a defence with a mazy dribble, Billy Bassett was a star turn from the moment he arrived on the scene as a teenager long before they were known by that name. He made his Albion debut in a 7-1 FA Cup win over Wednesbury Old Athletic on 15 October 1887, in the season West Brom won the competition for the first time. In his Albion career he played in three FA Cup finals, winning twice and losing once. Against which club did he both win and lose an FA Cup final?

482. Bassett's first West Bromwich Albion goal also came in that 1887-88 cup competition against a Midlands club who were also the team against whom he scored more Football League goals than any other. Who were they?

483. His first League goal for the Throstles arrived in the second match the club played in the League, a 2-1 away win on 15 September 1888. Who was it against?
A. Accrington B. Derby County C. Notts County D. Stoke

484. Billy Bassett's only FA Cup hat-trick came against the club that eventually became Blackpool. What were they called when his hat-trick, in his last season, helped to sink them 8-0 on 28 January 1899?

485. His delightful trickery and superb passing gained him 16 England caps on the right wing and brought him eight goals. Half of those matches were against one country. Which one?

486. Against which club from Lancashire that exited the Football League at the end of the century did Billy Bassett score three times in Albion's biggest win in their history – 12-0 on 4 April 1892?

487. Which club ground was the only one on which Bassett scored in two internationals for England?
A. Ewood Park B. Goodison Park C. Molineux D. the Victoria Ground

488. Which was the only ground on which Billy Bassett scored a hat-trick for West Brom and an international goal for England? The England goal came in a 6-1 win over Ireland in 1891, while the Albion goals came in an 8-0 win in 1893.

489. Billy Bassett's only rival in the battle to be called Mr West Brom was Fred Everiss, but Fred never played for them. What role at the club did Billy perform between 1908 and 1937?

490. When he died in 1937, 100,000 people filled the streets of West Bromwich for his funeral. His death came just two days before a vital Albion game which they lost, according to some because the players were unable to function properly. What game did they lose 4-1, and to which opponents?

491. Known to one and all at the Albion as Bomber, Tony Brown dominated events at the Hawthorns for 20 years between 1961 and 1981, breaking the club's records for appearances and goals in both the Football League and the FA Cup. Naturally, he scored on his debut, in a 2-1 League win at the Hawthorns on 28 September 1963 – against which club?

492. Probably playing for a less glamorous club cost Brown a number of international caps. The one he got came in an underwhelming 0-0 Wembley draw on 19 May 1971 – with which nation?

493. Brown was Division One's top scorer just once, when he netted 28 times to land the prize. In which season?

494. Of the 218 League goals to choose from, perhaps the most vital came at Boundary Park, Oldham on 24 April 1976, the last day of the season, when his stunning volley produced the game's only goal and sent 15,000 Baggies home with the promotion they craved. For what other reason might he have especially enjoyed it?

495. One city suffered significantly from Brown's striking credentials when, on 5 January 1974, he scored an FA Cup hat-trick in a 4-0 third round away win against one of the city's clubs, and then exactly one week later went one better by getting all four when Albion won away 4-1 against the city's other club. Which city suffered the hit?
A. Birmingham B. Manchester C. Nottingham D. Sheffield

496. When West Brom won the League Cup in 1965-66, Tony Brown scored in every round and also registered his only hat-trick in the competition in a 4-2 away win on 15 December 1965 – against which club in a second-leg tie?

497. His first hat-trick came against Sunderland, and he also scored one against their neighbours Newcastle United in a 6-1 Baggies win, but against which club did his Hawthorns hat-trick produce a 4-3 win in a thrilling encounter on 6 March 1971?

498. Who were the only club against whom Brown scored two League hat-tricks, coming in the same month of December of 1966 and 1970, each time assisted by a penalty?

499. His last League goal for Albion and his last League Cup goal for the club came against the same club in consecutive months in the autumn of 1979, while his final goal came in an FA Cup third round replay in London on 8 January 1980. Which two clubs were involved?

500. In 1974-75 and 1975-76, Brown scored from the penalty spot in consecutive FA Cup ties in different seasons against the same club. When he left West Bromwich Albion he became another club's top League scorer in 1981-82. These two clubs could hardly be further apart geographically. Who were they?

51   12 TOP THROSTLES
NO 5: TOMMY GLIDDEN

501.   Tommy Glidden captained Albion from the wing to their unique promotion
       and FA Cup double in 1930-31, making 445 Football League appearances
       and scoring 135 goals in his West Brom career. His debut, on 25 November
       1922, was a winning one – Albion took both points in a 1-0 win on which
       ground?
       A. Bramall Lane B. Goodison Park C. The Hawthorns D. Roker Park

502.   He had to wait a while for his first goal for the club, but when it arrived, in
       a 2-1 win at the Hawthorns on 30 March 1925, it was in front of the lowest
       home crowd of the season, just less than 10,000. Which Yorkshire club
       were their opponents that day?
       A. Huddersfield Town B. Leeds United C. Sheffield United
       D. Sheffield Wednesday

503.   Tommy Glidden scored in the FA Cup for West Brom against four clubs.
       Bristol City, Bradford Park Avenue and Huddersfield Town constituted the
       first three, but the most vital goal of his career came in the 1930-31 run to
       Wembley. It was the only goal in which round against which club?

504.   A feature of Albion's side in those years was Glidden's prolific partnership
       with the club's inside right – so much so that they were known as 'the twins'
       to Throstles fans. Who was his esteemed partner who scored 145 goals in
       414 Football League games for West Bromwich Albion?

505.   In 1928-29, Tommy Glidden was West Brom's joint top League goalscorer
       with 21 to his name. He shared the prize with someone who sports the same
       initials as the answer to the last question. Who was he?

506.   In the 1925-26 season, Glidden was on the scoresheet in two high-scoring
       Albion wins at the Hawthorns – the first in October and the second in
       November. They beat a club from the capital 7-1 and a club from Lancashire
       5-3. The clubs share their colours. Who were they?

507.   At one point, Tommy Glidden missed just 13 League games in eight seasons
       – some feat when you consider the factors involved all those years ago.
       In which two 1930s seasons did he appear in all 42 of the club's League
       games?

508.   Against which club did he hit four goals for the only time in his career,
       in a 6-2 home win on 26 October 1929?
       A. Sheffield Wednesday B. Southampton C. Stoke City D. Swansea Town

509.   The last of two away hat-tricks for West Brom in the League came in a
       4-2 win in Lancashire on 3 September 1932. Which club did they beat?

510.   Tommy served the club off the field when his playing days came to an end
       in 1936. He performed one role between 1936 and 1939, and another from
       1951 until his death in 1974. What were those two roles?

511. If it came to a war, Albion were ready for any eventuality. Later on they had a 'bomber', but before that their own 'tank' in the shape of front man Derek Kevan who, after joining the club in 1953 from Bradford Park Avenue for the sum of £3,000, went on to score 157 Football League goals in 262 games. Kevan scored two on his debut when Albion won 2-0 at home on 24 August 1955, and the club against whom he scored them were also the only one he put five past, in a 6-2 home win on 19 March 1960. Who were they?

512. Kevan scored a hat-trick or better against eight League clubs. The first of them came in London on 4 October 1958 but sadly didn't count for anything because West Brom lost the game 4-3 – on which ground?
A. Highbury B. Stamford Bridge C. Upton Park D. White Hart Lane

513. He also scored on his debut in international football, in a 2-1 England win at Wembley on 6 April 1957, and the following April, against the same country, produced the only occasion when he scored twice in a game for England when they were 4-0 winners away from home. Which country did they beat?

514. Kevan was Albion's top League scorer by himself five times and jointly once, and shared the divisional honours with Ray Crawford of Ipswich Town when both of them scored 33 Football League goals – in which season?

515. After a difference of opinion with manager Archie Macaulay, Kevan moved on in March 1963, but he made his point emphatically in his last game with a hat-trick in a 6-1 home win over which club on 9 March 1963?

516. Derek Kevan scored for his country in two World Cup matches in Sweden in 1958, and later had a strange experience against a Latin American country. On 24 May 1959, England lost 2-1 in Latin America and Kevan scored. Almost two years later, in his last game for England, they beat the same country 8-0 at Wembley and he didn't score any of them! Which country were England's opponents, the only one outside the British Isles against which Kevan played both home and away? A. Chile B. Mexico C. Peru D. Uruguay

517. In the FA Cup, Kevan scored 16 goals in 29 games in an Albion shirt. Five of them came against the same cluB. three in a 3-2 Hawthorns third round win in 1959-60 and the other two in a 5-1 away win at the same stage in 1962-63. Which club conceded the five goals to him?
A. Plymouth Argyle B. Portsmouth C. Port Vale D. Preston North End

518. Kevan's hat-tricks included those in two games that Albion won 7-1 – the first away in April 1960 and the second at home in the same month two years later, when he got four. The two beaten clubs both begin with B. Who were they?

519. Two more hat-tricks arrived on home soil in September 1962, the first a four-timer in a 6-1 win over a London club and the second in a 5-4 thriller against a Lancastrian club. The clubs share the same colours. Who were they?

520. Derek Kevan ended up playing for eight clubs. They constituted Bradford Park Avenue, Chelsea, Crystal Palace, Luton Town, Manchester City, Peterborough Utd, Stockport County and West Bromwich Albion. For which of those eight clubs did he have the best strike rate in League football?

521. When the 'new king' was plucked from Hayes in 1977, Ronnie Allen had a hard job to get the £5,000 out of the directors' tightly clenched fingers – so much so that he offered to buy Cyrille Regis with his own money! It didn't come to that, but it didn't take long to see that Allen had unearthed a diamond of a centre forward for next to nothing. Regis scored twice on his Albion debut, a 4-0 League Cup win at the Hawthorns on 31 August 1977 – against which Yorkshire opposition?
A. Barnsley B. Doncaster Rovers C. Huddersfield Town
D. Rotherham United

522. So exciting was his first Football League goal that it caused the Hawthorns to erupt. Albion won the game 2-1 on 3 September 1977, against which northern club?

523. How many seasons during his time at West Brom between 1977 and 1984 was Regis the club's leading League goalscorer?

524. He received four of his five England caps while at West Brom – the first two when he came on as a substitute against Northern Ireland and Wales in 1982 for the same player, who gained fame as the first million-pound player in the Football League. Who was he?

525. Cyrille Regis scored 26 goals in the two domestic cup competitions for West Bromwich Albion, but as an Albion player there were just two clubs against which he found the net in both the FA Cup and the League Cup. They met each other in a 1991 FA Cup semi-final. Who are they?

526. In 1978-79, Regis scored for the Albion in the UEFA Cup against two clubs who represent cities beginning with B. Who were they?

527. His three League hat-tricks for the Baggies all came against city clubs that have won the League Cup but have never won the FA Cup or a league title. Who were the three clubs?

528. Which manager earned the wrath of Albion fans by letting Cyrille Regis go to Coventry City for the bargain price of £300,000?

529. His last League goal came at the Hawthorns in a 4-0 win in front of a paltry 11,720 fans on the first day of September 1984. Whom did they beat that day?
A. Leicester City B. Luton Town C. Sunderland D. Watford

530. After landing a coveted FA Cup winners' medal in 1987 with Coventry City, Regis went on to play for four more Premier and Football League clubs. Who were they?

531. Leaving out of the reckoning a certain cricketer, Billy 'Ginger' Richardson was the most famous WG in English sporting circles – a man who couldn't stop scoring goals. From which club in the north-east did he arrive at the Albion in 1929?
A. Darlington B. Gateshead C. Hartlepools United D. South Shields

532. Richardson's debut at the Hawthorns on Boxing Day that year coincided with a 6-1 win over which visitors from the capital, with WG wasting no time in getting on the scoresheet?
A. Charlton Athletic B. Chelsea C. Millwall D. Spurs

533. He was unfortunate to receive just one cap for England, and it came on 18 May 1935 in a 1-0 away win in which city?
A. Amsterdam B. Berlin C. Lisbon D. Paris

534. Between 4 February and 1 April in the 1932-33 season, in how many consecutive West Brom Football League games did Richardson score?

535. In 1935-36, he smashed Albion's goalscoring record and scored more times than any other player in the four divisions of English League football. How many goals did he score in his 41 League appearances?

536. Richardson's 34 FA Cup appearances for West Brom yielded 26 goals, with two of them coming in the 1931 final at Wembley. He scored two hat-tricks in the competition, the first in a 7-1 win over a Yorkshire club in the fourth round of the 1934-35 season and the second in a 3-2 win in the same round in 1936-37, against one of the four sides in the first question. Who were the defeated clubs?

537. WG Richardson was the first Albion man to hit 200 goals, and no player has joined him there since. In how many seasons was he the club's leading League goalscorer?

538. John McIntyre of Blackburn Rovers had scored four goals in five minutes against Everton in 1922, and it looked unlikely that anyone would repeat the feat. Then, on 7 November 1931, along came WG to do so in a 5-1 win in London against which club?

539. It was a great feeling if you were an Albion fan at Christmas of 1932, because on the 24th WG Richardson got a hat-trick in a 4-3 Hawthorns win and then, on Boxing Day, in another home game, he got three more in a 5-1 win. The two beaten clubs came from the east Midlands and the north-east. Who were they?

540. WG Richardson scored four times in League games at the Hawthorns against Derby County, Leeds United and Middlesbrough. Apart from the answer to question eight, he scored four times away from home on one other ground, in the 1935-36 season. On which one?
A. Ewood Park B. Fratton Park C. Hillsborough D. Villa Park

12 TOP THROSTLES
NO 9: BOBBY ROBSON

541. Both on the pitch as a player and off it as a manager, Bobby Robson was a class act who gave Albion great service in the first capacity between 1956 and 1962. His West Brom career was bookended by two spells at another club for whom he played 344 times in the Football League. Who were they?

542. His debut for Albion and his last game for the club were contrasting affairs at the Hawthorns. West Brom were beaten heavily at home in his first game, on 10 March 1956, by 4-0 – to which City?
A. Birmingham City B. Cardiff City C. Manchester City D. Stoke City

543. Before March 1956 was out, Robson had scored his first goal for West Brom, in a 3-1 away win against one of the four clubs mentioned in the last question. Which one?

544. Bobby Robson started out at the Hawthorns as a free-scoring inside forward, but he gradually reverted very successfully to being the string puller in midfield in an attack-minded side. His 56 League goals for the club included a hat-trick in a 6-2 away win against which Midlands club on 12 April 1958?

545. He had gone one better on an earlier occasion when he nabbed four in a 5-1 win over a Lancastrian club at the Hawthorns on 28 December 1957. Who were they?
A. Blackpool B. Bolton Wanderers C. Burnley D. Preston North End

546. Robson scored four times in his 20 outings for England, making a dream debut in a 4-0 Wembley win on 27 November 1957 in which he scored two of the goals – against which nation?
A. Belgium B. France C. Italy D. West Germany

547. His other two England goals also came in magnificent performances in successive games at Wembley in April and May 1961. Which two nations were slaughtered 9-3 and 8-0 by a rampant England?

548. Bobby Robson scored five FA Cup goals for West Brom against four sides. Against which one of these four did he score both away and at home in a 3-3 draw and a 5-1 replay win in the 1957-58 season?
A. Blackpool B. Doncaster Rovers C. Nottingham Forest D. Sheffield United

549. We now come to Robson's last League game for the club, on 28 April 1962, when he went out with a bang by scoring one of the Albion's goals in a 7-1 thrashing of which club from Lancashire?

550. Why might Bobby Robson have felt elated with just a tinge of sadness on the afternoon of 8 April 1978?

551. Arguably the greatest player in the club's history, Bryan Robson was dynamism personified and influenced everything that happened in a game in which he was involved from the middle of the park. On which ground did he make his Albion bow, in a 3-1 away win on 12 April 1975?
A. Bloomfield Road B. Bootham Crescent C. Meadow Lane
D. The Manor Ground

552. Robson's first West Brom goal arrived in a 2-0 win at the Hawthorns exactly a week after his debut. It came against a club that were about to be relegated from Division Two alongside Sheffield Wednesday and Millwall. Who were they?

553. Who were the only Scottish club against which Bryan Robson scored during his time at West Bromwich Albion?
A. Celtic B. Hearts C. Rangers D. St Mirren

554. How many England caps did Bryan Robson gain during his time at West Brom?
A. 11 B. 12 C. 13 D. 14

555. On 16 March 1977, Bryan Robson scored his only hat-trick for the club in a 4-0 win at the Hawthorns – against which club?

556. He scored just once for England while at the Albion, and it came in his last international as a West Brom player, in Scandinavia on 9 September 1981 – against which country?
A. Denmark B. Finland C. Norway D. Sweden

557. During his time at West Brom, Bryan Robson's two League Cup goals came against the same London club, in a 1-1 home draw and a 1-0 away win in the 1979-80 season. Whom did the Albion beat 2-1 on aggregate?

558. Robson also scored two goals for West Bromwich Albion in the FA Cup, and they came against clubs in the east of the country that are separated by about 40 miles – in wins at the Hawthorns by 3-2 in 1975-76 and by 3-1 in 1980-81. Which two clubs did they knock out of the competition?

559. It might have been a good day for the club's coffers when ex-Baggies manager Ron Atkinson spirited Robson away to Old Trafford in the autumn of 1981, but it was a terrible day because the Albion lost their talisman. The fee was a new British record. What was it?

560. Inside a year following his departure, Robson had returned to the Hawthorns twice with his new club, scoring on both occasions – true or false?

57

12 TOP THROSTLES NO 11: BOB TAYLOR

561. Bob Taylor wasn't the greatest player to appear for the club but he scored a stack of goals, and the timing of those goals was important because they were vital in two promotion pushes nearly a decade apart and gave supporters starved of anything to get excited about the desire to get off their seats and shout again. The letter B figures extensively in Bob Taylor's career. From which club did he come in 1992?

562. He hadn't been at the Hawthorns more than a couple of months following his debut on 1 February 1992 before he had scored against five Bs. The two against Birmingham City went down well with Baggies fans, and he also found the net against Bournemouth, Bury and Bolton Wanderers. Naturally, that 2-0 debut win at the Hawthorns also involved a B. Which one?

563. In Albion's 1992-93 promotion out of the third tier of English football, Taylor was a revelation. He took the club's player of the year award, missed none of their 46 League games and scored how many goals in the League that season?

564. Only one man surpassed his total of League goals. Who was he?

565. Those Bs are back again! To which club was Taylor loaned before signing for them in 1998, and against which club did he score his first Albion goal second time around, in a 2-2 draw in Yorkshire on 8 April 2000 after coming back to West Brom?

566. Which manager brought him to the club initially; for which manager did he score those goals that got Albion up in 1992-93; and which manager returned him to the fold in 2000?

567. Bob Taylor scored six times in the League Cup for West Bromwich Albion, against four clubs. Two of them were Plymouth Argyle and Chelsea, while the other two are linked as towns through one of them being synonymous with the production of items worn at one end of the body while the other is known for the manufacture of products worn at the opposite end of the body. Who were the two clubs?

568. Bob Taylor's lone hat-trick in Albion's colours came in a 4-4 Hawthorns draw with which club on 12 March 1996?

569. He was on the mark for West Bromwich Albion against three clubs in the FA Cup. Derby County were one of them, but the other two were non-League sides from different ends of the alphabet in the first two rounds of the 1992-93 season. Who were they?

570. Although Bob Taylor did play four times in the following season, he really went out in a blaze of glory when West Brom clinched an unlikely promotion to the Premier League in 2001-02, scoring three vital goals in the last four games. He got the only goal away to another Midlands club, the goal in a 1-1 home draw with a Yorkshire club, and finally one of the two that enabled the club to clinch promotion at home against a London club. Who were the three opponents?

12 TOP THROSTLES
NO 12: JOHN WILE

571. John Wile and Ally Robertson were at the heart of the Albion defence throughout the 1970s, giving performances beyond the call of duty on a regular basis. Wile's total of Football League appearances for the club was a nice round figure. What was it?

572. Wile played for one other club before the Albion, and when he left the Hawthorns in 1983 he returned to that same club as player-manager, eventually ending up playing 205 times in the Football League for them. Who were they?

573. Against which club from Lancashire did John Wile make his Albion debut in a 1-1 draw at the Hawthorns on 19 December 1970?
A. Blackburn Rovers B. Blackpool C. Bolton Wanderers D. Burnley

574. His first West Bromwich Albion goal came in a 3-3 away draw on 27 February 1971 – on which ground?
A. The Dell B. Goodison Park C. Maine Road D. Turf Moor

575. Outside the Football League and the domestic cup competitions, John Wile scored one other West Brom goal, and it came in a 1-1 home draw against which club in the Anglo-Italian tournament on 26 May 1971?

576. Which London ground was the only one on which he scored twice in a West Brom game, coming in a 3-3 draw on 12 November 1977?
A. Highbury B. Loftus Road C. Stamford Bridge D. Upton Park

577. John Wile's record of missing just 14 League games in 11 seasons is hard to believe and a phenomenal testament to his courage and resolution. In how many seasons at West Bromwich Albion did he appear in every League game?

578. By a strange quirk, he played for Albion in 42 FA Cup ties and 42 League Cup ties, scoring twice in each competition. In the League Cup his goals came against Rotherham United and Coventry City, while in the FA Cup they came in replays in 1974-75 and 1978-79, against two clubs that share the same colours but come from different sides of the Pennines. Who were they?

579. Which Midlands club were the only side against whom Wile scored home and away in the same season? Both games were in the 1976-77 season and both ended in 1-1 draws.

580. There is a picture of John Wile that famously reflects his approach on the field. Can you describe it and give the occasion on which it was taken?

581.   On which ground have West Bromwich Albion played in four FA Cup finals, winning two and losing two?

582.   On which two Midlands grounds did Albion play Aston Villa in the FA Cup semi-final of 1957?

583.   Which is the only ground on which West Brom have played an FA Cup final in two different centuries?

584.   The most southerly ground on which the Baggies have contested an FA Cup semi-final has been an unlucky place for them because they lost on all three visits there, in 1937, 1978 and 1982. At least they won't lose there again, because it no longer exists! Which ground was it?

585.   The FA Cup final of 1912, in which Albion were involved, went to a replay. On which Yorkshire ground did that replay take place?
A. Bramall Lane   B. Elland Road   C. Hillsborough   D. Leeds Road

586.   What was the last ground on which West Brom won an FA Cup semi-final?

587.   On which ground have Albion got a 75 per cent success rate in FA Cup finals?

588.   On which Lancastrian ground have Albion played in an FA Cup semi-final just once, against Everton in 1907?
A. Burnden Park   B. Deepdale   C. Ewood Park   D. Turf Moor

589.   On which ground have West Bromwich Albion played in three FA Cup semi-finals, losing in 1889 and 1969 but winning a semi-final replay in 1912?

590.   When Albion got to Wembley in 1931, they won their semi-final at a ground on which they were playing a semi-final for the first time. Which ground was it?

591. West Brom participated in their first FA Cup tie on 10 November 1883, losing 2-0 at home – to which club?
A. Aston Unity B. Druids C. Junction Street School D. Wednesbury Town

592. Jim Bayliss became the first Albion player to score an FA Cup hat-trick when he did so in their 6-0 home win over which club on 13 February 1886?
A. Old Carthusians B. Old Westminsters C. Wednesbury Old Athletic
D. Wolves

593. Which club did West Brom run into a total of seven times, including a replay, between 1884-85 and 1895-96 in the FA Cup competition?
A. Aston Villa B. Blackburn Rovers C. Preston North End D. The Wednesday

594. On 2 March 1889, West Brom recorded their biggest ever win in the FA Cup when they won 10-1 away from home against which club?
A. Chatham B. Burton Wanderers C. Derby Junction
D. Mitchell St George's

595. In the 1889-90 season Albion lost 3-1 away at Accrington in the first round of the FA Cup. A week later, the match was played again at the same venue, Albion going down 3-0 this time. Why was it replayed?

596. In the 1912-13 season West Brom drew their first FA Cup tie 1-1 at home to West Ham United. The second match in London also ended level at 2-2. Rather unfairly, the clubs met for a third time on a neutral London ground, with Albion going down 3-0. Where was the match played?
A. Craven Cottage B. Griffin Park C. Stamford Bridge D. White Hart Lane

597. West Brom's longest journey for an FA Cup tie was in the 1899-1900 season, when they lost 2-1. In 1907-08 they returned to the same ground, this time losing 1-0. Which club knocked them out on both occasions?

598. On their way to the FA Cup final of 1912, Albion won two home ties by 3-0 against two London clubs who share the same colours. Who were they?

599. Who were the only club to play West Brom three times in this period, and beat them on each occasion?
A. Derby County B. Everton C. Liverpool D. Sheffield United

600. In the first round in 1897-98 and 1898-99, Albion won home ties against two Lancastrian clubs associated with towers. The first of them had the word in their name, while the second, playing before their name change, had seen their tower open a few years before. Who were the two clubs?

601. Which Midlands club put paid to West Brom's FA Cup hopes in successive seasons in 1920-21 and 1921-22?
A. Birmingham B. Leicester City C. Nottingham Forest D. Notts County

602. On their way to winning the trophy in 1930-31, Albion took three games to get past Charlton Athletic at the first hurdle, finally doing so by 3-1 on which neutral Midlands ground?
A. Filbert Street B. Molineux C. St Andrew's D. Villa Park

603. Over this period, four clubs from the capital knocked West Brom out of the FA Cup. Which one of the following five didn't do so? Arsenal, Charlton Athletic, Chelsea, Spurs and West Ham United.

604. The record attendance at the Hawthorns was broken when 64,612 saw the Albion draw 1-1 with which club on 21 February 1925?

605. West Bromwich Albion visited Wales for the first time for an FA Cup tie on 11 January 1930 and wished they hadn't after losing 2-0 to a side from the third level of the Football League. Who beat them that day, ending their interest in the cup?
A. Cardiff City B. Newport County C. Swansea Town D. Wrexham

606. That wasn't the only time in this period that Albion went out to third-flight opposition. Which Third Division North side, who reached the semi-final from that division in 1955, beat West Brom 3-2 in the fourth round in the 1937-38 season?

607. Who scored in Albion's first four FA Cup matches in 1928-29, including a four-timer against Bradford Park Avenue in a 6-0 win at the Hawthorns in the fifth round on 16 February 1929?
A. Joe Carter B. Jimmy Cookson C. Tommy Glidden D. George James

608. In this period Albion twice enjoyed 7-1 home wins in the FA Cup. They came in the fourth round of 1934-35, on the road to Wembley, and in the third round of 1936-37. The first of them was against Yorkshire opposition who reached the final themselves the following season, while the second was against a non-League side from the north-east. The two clubs share the first letter of their names. Who were they?

609. West Brom had two 5-1 away wins in FA Cup ties in the 1930s: the first against a club not far from Manchester in the fifth round of 1934-35; and the second in a third round replay in 1938-39 against a club within the city of Manchester itself. Which two clubs did they beat?

610. Both Sheffield clubs won the FA Cup after putting West Brom out in this period, in 1925 and 1935. The only other time that the Albion lost to the eventual winners came in 1938-39, the last season before the war, when they went down 2-0 away in the fourth rounD. to which southern club?

611. The teams that put West Brom out of the competition in 1946, 1947, 1949 and 1957 all went on to win it, and on two more occasions the team that knocked them out reached the final. Which four clubs won the trophy after pointing WBA to the exit?

612. When the Albion won the FA Cup themselves in 1954, along the way they beat one Yorkshire club 4-0 in the fourth round at the Hawthorns. Who were they?
A. Barnsley B. Doncaster Rovers C. Huddersfield Town
D. Rotherham United

613. Who scored West Brom's first post-Second World War FA Cup hat-trick when he got all their goals in a 3-0 home win over Chelsea in the fifth round in 1948-49?

614. A club from the north-east lost at home to Albion twice in the FA Cup, first by 3-1 in the fourth round of 1948-49 and then by 2-0 at the same stage in 1951-52. On the first occasion they lost on their own ground, but on the second occasion they borrowed St James' Park from Newcastle United to earn more money from a gate of 38,681, which compared to that of 16,885 from the first encounter. Who were they?

615. With which Midlands club did West Bromwich Albion draw 3-3 at the Hawthorns in the fourth round of 1957-58, before pulling out all the stops to win the replay 5-1?
A. Birmingham City B. Leicester City C. Nottingham Forest D. Wolves

616. Against which London club did West Brom play in five consecutive FA Cup ties, four games being needed to separate the sides in the fourth round of 1952-53, when Albion were eventually eliminated before bouncing back to win 1-0 at the Hawthorns the following season, in the Baggies' first game on the road to Wembley?

617. Albion won that game with an own goal by the visitors' centre half, who later went on to win the trophy as a manager with another London club in 1964. Who was he?

618. In the 1954-55 season, when West Brom were defending Cup holders, they won 1-0 at Bournemouth before losing 4-2 to Charlton Athletic at the Valley. All three of their goals came from an unlikely source and constituted one third of all the goals he scored for West Bromwich Albion. Who was he?

619. Which city's two clubs bookended Albion's FA Cup story in 1957-58, the first losing to the Baggies 5-1 in the third round and the second winning 1-0 in a replay after a 2-2 sixth round draw?

620. The only two sides to knock Albion out of the FA Cup twice in this period met each other in the 1946 FA Cup final. Who were they?

621. In 1962 and 1965, West Brom exited the FA Cup competition at the hands of the eventual winners of the trophy. Which two clubs were they?

622. The Albion's biggest FA Cup win of the decade came by 5-1 after their longest journey on 5 January 1963. Where did they win?

623. After not bothering to enter the new League Cup competition in its first five years, West Brom decided to give it a go in 1965-66, and were rewarded by a trophy win! Which Midlands club were their very first opponents in the competition at the Hawthorns on 22 September 1965, in a game the home side won 3-1?

624. The Albion went on to be a real force in that competition, reaching the finals in 1966, 1967 and 1970. Which three Uniteds did they put out in the semi-finals in those years?

625. An unusual thing happened in the 1966-67 season when Albion won 3-1 away against the same club in both cup competitions. Who was it?
A. Newport County B. Northampton Town C. Norwich City
D. Nottingham Forest

626. As Albion won the trophy in 1968, it meant that they were eliminated from the FA Cup on nine occasions over this decade. Nine different clubs beat them, eight of which have won the FA Cup. Their first conquerors in 1960-61, who won a third round tie 3-1, have never got as far as the semi-final stage. Who were they?

627. When Albion won the FA Cup in 1968, they won away against two southern clubs not a million miles apart in successive rounds, by 3-2 in a fourth round replay and by 2-1 in the fifth round. Which two clubs did they eliminate from the competition?

628. A powerful Liverpool unit awaited them in the quarter-finals that year, but the teams couldn't be separated after two games, with Albion edging the third encounter 2-1 – on which neutral ground?

629. What linked the three clubs that West Brom beat in rounds four, five and six in the FA Cup of 1968-69, with a 1-0 home win being sandwiched between two 2-1 away wins?

630. Nottingham Forest were unable to play their home League Cup tie against West Bromwich Albion at the City Ground on 3 September 1968. Where did Albion win 3-2?
A. The Baseball Ground B. Field Mill C. Filbert Street D. Meadow Lane

631. Which London club eliminated Albion from successive League Cup competitions in 1970-71 and 1971-72, going on to win the trophy on the first occasion?

632. Which club did West Bromwich Albion play four times in the FA Cup third round of 1972-73 when the second of those games was abandoned due to fog, Albion finally winning 3-1 at neutral Filbert Street at the fourth time of asking?

633. Which player scored the only cup hat-trick in this period for West Brom when he scored three of the four goals they put past Notts County without reply in the FA Cup third round on 5 January 1974?

634. Four clubs from the capital fell victim to West Bromwich Albion in the League Cup over this decade. They were Charlton Athletic, Fulham, Millwall and QPR. But which one of the four also knocked Albion out of the competition in 1975-76?

635. The FA Cup winners of 1976, 1978 and 1980 all beat West Brom in winning the trophy. Who were the three?

636. In the League Cup in 1973-74, as a Second Division club, Albion were drawn at home to a side from the division above them, raising their game to beat their red and white-striped visitors 2-1. They were drawn at home to red and white-striped opposition in the next round, this time to a club from the Fourth Division who beat them 3-1. Who were the two opponents of contrasting fortunes?

637. Which northern club did West Brom meet in consecutive FA Cup ties in different seasons, going out away to them in the fourth round of 1974-75 but beating them 3-1 at home in the third round of 1975-76?

638. In 1978-79, West Bromwich Albion met Leeds United five times in cup competition. After a 3-3 draw at the Hawthorns in the FA Cup fourth round, Albion ran out 2-0 winners in the replay. What was odd about the game?

639. Against the same opposition in the League Cup in 1978-79, three attritional games produced just one goal and Albion didn't score it. On which neutral ground did Leeds United go through?
A. Anfield B. Goodison Park C. Maine Road D. Old Trafford

640. In 1977-78, on their route to an FA Cup semi-final, West Brom knocked out the holders of the trophy in the fourth round, winning 3-2 after extra time in a replay at the Hawthorns. Who were they?

641. Apart from the 1981-82 season, when the Albion reached the semi-finals of both domestic cup competitions, this decade was a hard watch for fans. How many seasons in a row did West Brom get knocked out of the FA Cup at the first hurdle?

642. In the League Cup they did show some grit with two great fightbacks. In the first of them in 1983-84 they trailed 3-0 after going down to London for the first leg, before turning things round to the tune of 5-1 at the Hawthorns in the second leg – against which club?

643. The second fightback in that competition came in the 1989-90 season, when they were beaten 3-1 at home before going through on away goals after coming out on top by 5-3 in the second leg in Yorkshire – against which club?

644. Which club went on to win the FA Cup for the only time in their history after beating West Brom 4-1 in the third round in 1988?

645. Who made a big contribution to the club's progress in the League Cup in 1985-86 when he grabbed both goals in a 2-2 draw at Port Vale, before doing the same in a 4-3 home win over Coventry City in the next round?

646. Which Midlands club ended Albion's prospects in the League Cup in both 1986-87 and 1989-90?
A. Aston Villa B. Birmingham City C. Derby County D. Nottingham Forest

647. Who were the only club that West Brom eliminated from both cup competitions over this period, beating them in the FA Cup in 1981-82 and the League Cup in 1985-86?

648. Which two clubs, one from London and the other from the Midlands, removed Albion from both domestic cup competitions over this period?

649. When Albion reached the League Cup semi-final in 1981-82, they won away in the capital against two clubs successively, beating the first of them 1-0 after two draws and the second by 3-1. Who were the two clubs?

650. A bit of giantkilling took place in the FA Cup on 18 February 1984. Unfortunately, it was at the Hawthorns, when which Third Division side who reached the semi-finals that year knocked Albion out 1-0?

WBA IN CUP COMPETITIONS 1990-2000

651.   If you thought the previous decade wasn't great where cups were concerned, this one left it far behind where depression was concerned. Over both domestic cup competitions, Albion had 20 chances to get beyond the first opposition they faced. How many times did they fail to do so?

652.   Perhaps the worst moment in the club's history came at the Hawthorns on 5 January 1991, when which non-League club left the Midlands with a passport to the fourth round of the FA Cup after beating Albion 4-2 in their own back yard?

653.   Albion got their own back to some extent where non-League clubs were concerned by thrashing one of them 6-0 in the third round the following season. Who were they?

654.   Who was the only West Bromwich Albion player to score a hat-trick in a cup tie for them in this period when he did so in the 1992-93 season? A. Kevin Donovan B. Simon Garner C. Andy Hunt D. Bob Taylor

655.   In the three successive seasons of 1994-95, 1995-96 and 1996-97, West Brom went out of the FA Cup at the hands of a side beginning with C. Who were the three clubs?

656.   When they beat Stoke City 3-1 at the Hawthorns in the FA Cup third round of 1997-98, you had to go back to 1992-93 to find the last time the Albion had won in that competition. Whose two goals were vital that day?

657.   How are Adams Park, the Shay and Stamford Bridge connected concerning West Brom in domestic cup football over this period?

658.   Over both domestic cup competitions in this period, West Brom came up against five clubs beginning with B. They comprised Blackburn Rovers, Bournemouth, Brentford, Bristol City and Bristol Rovers. Four of the five knocked Albion out, but which one of the five did they beat in the League Cup in 1993-94?

659.   Who were the only club to go on to win the FA Cup after putting Albion out of the competition in this decade?

660.   The two West Bromwich Albion goalscorers in the 2-2 League Cup second leg home draw with Swindon Town on 28 August 1991 sound like someone paying a compliment to the character of a man who lived between 1564 and 1616! Who were the scorers?

661. Albion were one of the 12 clubs from the Midlands and north-west that formed the Football League, and on 8 September 1888 they won their first game in the competition by 2-0 away from home against the club that eventually finished bottom. Who were they?

662. Tom Pearson became the first man to score a League hat-trick for the club when he got four in their 6-3 win over which club on 4 November 1889, before repeating the feat exactly in a 5-2 win against the same opposition on 6 November 1893?

663. What was Albion's highest Football League position in the 12 seasons between 1888 and 1900?

664. In those first few seasons, Albion lost to Accrington, Burnley and Preston North End by the same rare scoreline. What was it?
A. 5-3 B. 5-4 C. 6-3 D. 6-4

665. In the 1892-93 season, Albion conceded eight goals in two League games for the only time in their history, losing 8-1 away on both occasions. The first was to a side from the north-east in October, the second to a Midlands club in November. Which two clubs slaughtered them?

666. One of the greatest transformations in League football involved West Bromwich Albion in the 1893-94 season. On 27 December they won 8-0 away in the Midlands, but three days later they lost 7-1 away in the north-west. Against which two clubs did they experience these contrasting situations?

667. West Brom were in dire straits when they kicked off at home in the last game of the 1894-95 season, when a defeat would have meant a likely relegation. A 6-0 win was just the stuff to give the troops and they survived. Which Yorkshire club suffered the defeat?

668. Why weren't West Bromwich Albion relegated when they finished bottom of the First Division in the 1895-96 season?

669. Tom Pearson was the club's leading goalscorer in each of their first five seasons of League football, but on two of those occasions he had to share the kudos – with which other Albion player?

670. West Brom's last two home games of this period had contrasting outcomes. On 14 April 1900 they drew 0-0, and just two days later they won 8-0. Both visitors came from the same city. Which one?

671. Although West Brom had finished bottom of the First Division twice before, there had been no Second Division to be relegated to the first time and a 'test match' saved them the second time. The new century brought the club's first experience of the drop in 1900-01. It hadn't looked likely, but they lost seven of their last eight games, and that did for them. The one they won was against the same team and by the same score as a later FA Cup final in which they participated. Whom did they beat and by what score?

672. It took the Albion just one season to restore their place at the top table when they lost just four times in taking the Division Two title. During that 1901-02 season they enjoyed a run of games without defeat that they would later equal but never surpass. How many?

673. After their promotion, the Albion began the 1902-03 season in fine style, winning eight of nine games in the autumn. After beating Middlesbrough on 17 January, they, as it proved, needed less than a point a game to win the title, but an awful run saw them eventually finish seventh. How many successive games did they lose?

674. A crowd of 28,536 had turned up to see them play Aston Villa on 28 February 1903, but their terrible form meant that when they finally won 3-0 on the last day of the season at home to Derby County, the match was witnessed by how many supporters, to the nearest thousand?

675. WBA were on a downward spiral, and 1903-04 saw them relegated again as bottom club. The northern club that accompanied them into the Second Division lost no time in getting back, winning the Division Two title in 1904-05 while West Bromwich Albion languished in tenth spot. Who were they?

676. Albion spent the next four seasons finishing fourth, fourth, fifth and third. In that last season of 1908-09, Bolton Wanderers went up as champions, but which London club sneaked into the second spot on goal average over Albion to deny them promotion?

677. When they finished fourth in 1906-07, Albion scored their highest goals tally to date. Who broke their record for top goalscorer in a season with 28 of their 83 goals? A. Fred Buck B. Adam Haywood C. Walter Jack D. Fred Shinton

678. After sliding to 11th place in 1909-10, West Brom were promoted as champions in 1910-11 after winning their last five games. The clincher on the final day of the season came from the penalty spot in a 1-0 home win over Huddersfield Town. The man who took it is one of the four possibles for the previous question. Which one?

679. Albion saw out the last four seasons before war intervened as a mid-table side in the top flight. Their top two goalscorers in 1913-14 and 1914-15 were both makes of cars. Who were they?

680. Which player became the first Albion man to score a hat-trick for the club in successive home games when he did so in wins of 6-1 and 4-0 over Doncaster Rovers and Burton United on 24 September and 8 October 1904?

681.   West Brom emerged from the First World War to play some of the best attacking football the League had yet seen, amazingly landing their only League title by a massive nine-point margin from Burnley despite losing ten games. They became the first club to win the League while scoring more than 100 goals. What was their total?

682.   Not content with breaking Albion's goalscoring record in that 1919-20 title-winning side with 37, which player also became the first WBA man to find the net five times in a League game when his nap hand helped them to an 8-0 win over Notts County at the Hawthorns on 25 October 1919?

683.   Albion's descent was sudden in 1920-21, when they finished 14th, scoring 50 fewer goals than the previous season! In October, visiting Lancashire and Yorkshire in successive away games, they lost 5-1 both times to the two clubs who went on to contest the 1928 FA Cup final. Who were they?

684.   By 1923-24, Albion had sunk to 16th in the League. On the season's last day they won 3-1 at home to Sheffield Utd, with all of the goals coming from a player who that morning had stood in third place in their League goalscorers' table but by late afternoon had won it with his treble. Who was he?
       A. Bobby Blood B. Joe Carter C. Stan Davies D. Fred Morris

685.   Unpredictable Albion had another superb season in 1924-25, missing out on the title by two points in a season in which one of their players scored in seven successive League games. Who pipped them to the title to retain their crown, and which player was on the mark seven games running? If you need a clue to the player, you need to add a scorer in the 1971 FA Cup final to another from the 1930 final and you've got it!

686.   Incredibly, partly due to a change in the offside law, in 1925-26 Albion fell 11 places down the League while scoring 21 more goals than they did when finishing second! The season's biggest win was by 7-1 at the Hawthorns on 24 October 1925, when they beat a London club who had joined the top flight three years before. Who were they?

687.   In 1926-27 West Brom were relegated with Leeds United, the only glimpse of a silver lining coming at the Hawthorns on 12 March 1927, when 50,392 turned up to see them win 6-2 – against which old rivals?

688.   Although they could only finish eighth in the Second Division in 1927-28, Albion did score 90 goals, with 38 of them going to a new player who broke their record for leading scorer in a season. Who was he?

689.   The 1928-29 season brought an improvement of just one place when Albion finished seventh. On 17 April 1929 they won 5-2 in London, with Tommy Glidden claiming a hat-trick. Against which club?
       A. Chelsea B. Clapton Orient C. Millwall D. Spurs

690.   West Brom managed sixth spot in Division Two in 1929-30, scoring the most goals in the League that season and breaking their own record for a season too. During the course of the season they twice scored seven at home, in 7-3 and 7-1 wins over clubs that have links to animals. Who were they?

691. In 1930-31, West Bromwich Albion became the only side to win promotion and the FA Cup in the same season. They finished the season as runners-up to Everton, holding off which London club by three points on the run-in?

692. Albion made a great start to the season by winning their opening four games, the third of which was won 6-3 away from home, with Jimmy Cookson claiming four of the goals. Whom did they beat?
A. Cardiff City B. Charlton Athletic C. Chesterfield D. Coventry City

693. When West Brom finished fourth in Division One in 1932-33, a 4-0 home win over Bolton Wanderers on 10 December 1932 produced three goalscorers whose names all began with R. Who were they?

694. One northern club had some interesting experiences on four occasions visiting the Hawthorns in the 1930s, losing 5-1, 6-5 and 6-4 before finally winning 6-1. Who were they?

695. Albion made a superb start to the new year with a 7-2 away win on 1 January 1934. On which ground?
A. Bramall Lane B. Ewood Park C. Fratton Park D. Maine Road

696. In the 1934-35 season, West Brom recorded 6-3 wins over both Leeds United and Middlesbrough, but also conceded nine goals for the first time in their history when going down 9-3 to which Midlands club on 8 December 1934? A. Aston Villa B. Birmingham C. Derby County D. Wolves

697. Although they scored more goals than they conceded, Albion escaped the drop by three points in the 1935-36 season. The two clubs that went down were the only two playing top-flight football who had not experienced relegation up to that point. Albion helped one of them on their way with an 8-1 hammering on 18 January 1936. Who were the two clubs?

698. In that 8-1 victory, two players scored hat-tricks. One of them was inevitably the great WG Richardson. Who scored the other one?
A. Walter Boyes B. Jack Mahon C. Teddy Sandford D. Stan Wood

699. After seven years in the top flight since their previous relegation, the long drop caught up with West Brom again in 1937-38. There has only been one club that has won the Football League in one season and been relegated the next, but that was the club that accompanied Albion on their downward journey at the end of that season, with both of them on 36 points. The previous season this side had totalled 57 points and 107 goals in winning the title. Who were they?

700. So, Albion played their last inter-war season in Division Two, finishing an underwhelming tenth. Towards the end of the season, after they had scored one goal in seven games, interest declined, and although they won their last game of the season 4-2 at home to Norwich City, it was watched by the club's lowest attendance for nine years. What was it?
A. 2,109 B. 3,109 C. 4,109 D. 5,109

71 WBA IN THE FOOTBALL LEAGUE 1946-1960

701. West Brom opened their first post-war season with a 3-2 away win at Swansea Town in Division Two, and a player making his debut for the club that day went on to create a record by scoring in each of the first six games of his career. Who was he?

702. When Albion visited Wales again four weeks later, they hammered Newport County 7-2, contributing to the relegation of both those Welsh clubs by the season's end. Four of the seven that day were scored by someone who would go on to win two titles at Portsmouth after leaving West Brom. Who was he?

703. Another striker, who went on to score more goals than anyone in the history of the Football League, got the very first goal of his career when Albion lost 3-1 at Leeds United on 21 February 1948. He scored just three more for Albion. Who was he?

704. West Bromwich Albion achieved their very welcome promotion out of Division Two in 1948-49, when they went up as runners-up. If they had drawn instead of losing by 2-1 when the eventual champions came to the Hawthorns on 5 March 1949, Albion would have won the title instead of which London club?

705. West Brom's first game back among the big boys was a 1-0 home win on 20 August 1949 – against which London club?
A. Arsenal B. Charlton Athletic C. Chelsea D. Fulham

706. On which away ground did Albion score 12 goals in the League by winning there 5-3 on New Year's Day of 1953 and by 7-3 on 16 September of that same year but in the following season?
A. Deepdale B. Hillsborough C. St James' Park D. Turf Moor

707. When a side reaches the FA Cup final, it often affects their league form for the rest of the season, and this phenomenon in 1953-54 stopped West Bromwich Albion becoming the first club to do the elusive double in the 20th century. They lost five of their last seven Football League fixtures to finish second to which club?

708. That disappointment was reflected in Albion's plunge from second to 17th in 1954-55, when they managed to ship 96 goals. It sounds like 25 September 1954 brought some entertainment to the Hawthorns – they beat Leicester City by 6-4, with which Albion inside forward scoring their only hat-trick?

709. Which Albion defender who went on to be an English international made his debut against Everton on 24 August 1955?

710. In the final three seasons of this period Albion were a good side, finishing fourth, fifth and fourth again. For the only occasion, the 1957-58 season produced a situation in which a club reached three figures in both the goals-for and goals-against columns. West Brom managed nine against them on 21 September 1957 in a 9-2 romp at the Hawthorns. Who were they?

711. After a dreadful start to the 1960-61 campaign when they lost their opening five matches, Albion made amends with a resounding 6-0 victory in the sixth game, at home to Newcastle United on 5 September 1960. They were assisted by a hat-trick from which player?
A. David Burnside B. Alec Jackson C. Derek Kevan D. Bobby Robson

712. Having lost their first five games in 1960-61, Albion duly won their last five in 1961-62, ending with a 7-1 thrashing on 28 April 1962 of which Lancastrian visitors beginning with B?
A. Blackburn Rovers B. Blackpool C. Bolton Wanderers D. Burnley

713. On 29 August in the 1962-63 season, Albion ran out 3-2 winners away from home on the only occasion they ever played in a top-flight league game on this ground. Which ground was it?

714. When Everton were beaten 4-2 at the Hawthorns on 31 March 1964, an Albion player who scored just five times for the club before moving on to Exeter City got three of those five in this one game. Who was he?

715. It had been all of 45 years since an Albion defender had registered three goals in a League game, but which player put that right on 12 September 1964, in a 5-2 win over Stoke City at the Hawthorns, with two of the goals coming from the penalty spot?

716. After sending fans home happy with that 7-1 home win on the last day of the 1961-62 season, the Albion did so again with the help of a Tony Brown hat-trick on the final day of the 1966-67 season, beating which northern club 6-1 at the Hawthorns?
A. Everton B. Leeds United C. Newcastle United D. Sunderland

717. On Armistice Day of 1967, West Bromwich Albion produced their biggest win for ten years when they won 8-1 at the Hawthorns. Of the four Lancastrian clubs mentioned in the second question, only one was still in the top flight in the 1967-68 season, and it was this one that went back north heavily defeated on that November day. Which one was it?

718. Albion's opening game of the 1969-70 season came at the Dell on 9 August 1969, when the supplier of both goals in a 2-0 win was someone making his debut who became the club's top goalscorer that season. Who was he?

719. Which club became the first for seven years to score seven times against West Brom when they beat them 7-0 in the penultimate game of the 1969-70 season?

720. Albion's top League goalscorer award over this ten-year period was shared on two occasions. Of the eight occasions when it wasn't shared, who was the only man besides Jeff Astle to win it three times?

721.   Which striker signed from Wolves, who eventually joined Bristol City, scored his first Albion goal in a 2-0 win against Crystal Palace at Selhurst Park on 9 October 1971?

722.   When West Bromwich Albion beat Chelsea 4-0 at the Hawthorns on 27 April 1972, it was the first of several instances when two players with the same surname scored for them in a game. Who were the two players involved?

723.   After finishing 17th and 16th in the decade's first two years, Albion finally succumbed to relegation in 1972-73, going down with which London club?

724.   They played their first game outside the top flight in almost a quarter of a century when they recorded a 3-2 win by the seaside on 25 August 1973. Where?

725.   West Brom spent three years at the second level before being assisted in climbing back up in 1975-76. By this time the 'three up, three down' system had been brought in and Albion, in third place, were the beneficiaries of the change. Sunderland won the race for the title with Albion sandwiched between two clubs, both beginning with B, one of which accompanied them on their upward journey while the other remained frustrated. Who were the two clubs?

726.   As new boys, Albion finished a very respectable seventh back in the big time in 1976-77, but did take one heavy hammering, by 7-0, away from home on 6 November 1976 against a club that would frustrate their cup ambitions the following season as well. Who were they?

727.   Over the decade there were numerous occasions on which fewer than 10,000 people attended an Albion away game, but all except one were outside the top flight. The exception came when a crowd of 9,938 saw them lose 1-0 to which Yorkshire club on 11 September 1971?

728.   Things have never again been quite as good as the 1978-79 season, when Albion finished third and garnered much publicity along the way with Ron Atkinson and his 'Three Degrees'. The football was great, with the biggest win coming on 21 October 1978, by 7-1 at the Hawthorns, and the most coverage in the media concerning their 5-3 away win on 30 December 1978. Which two clubs did they beat?

729.   How many times was Tony Brown Albion's top League goalscorer over this period?

730.   Which player who was later transferred to Manchester United opened his Albion account with a goal in a 4-4 home draw with Bolton Wanderers on 18 March 1980, and which record Albion signing came up with the other three goals?

WBA IN THE FOOTBALL LEAGUE 1980-1990

731. The decade started well enough with Albion in fourth place in the top flight, but in 1981-82 they sank as far as 17th and the future didn't look so bright. In that season Notts County, who were enjoying their first season at that level for 55 years, won 4-2 at the Hawthorns on 24 March 1982. Albion's two goalscorers had names connected to monarchy. Who were they?

732. When West Brom won 2-1 against Spurs at White Hart Lane on 7 November 1981, one of their goals came from a man who would later manage that club. Who was he?

733. The 1982-83 season brought a mid-table finish, four consecutive 0-0 draws and the lowest average attendance since 1914-15. The following season was even worse as Albion nosedived to 17th in the table. On the first day of that season they lost 4-3 at Aston Villa, but the following month saw them win by the same score at Ipswich. The first man with a surname starting with Z in the club's history found the net in both those games. Who was he?

734. Which striker scored his first hat-trick for the Albion when they beat Nottingham Forest 4-1 on 13 October 1984?

735. The blow finally came in 1985-86, when Albion were relegated in bottom place with just four wins from their 42 matches. Tough times indeed! If there was any crumb of comfort in the situation, it was in the name of one of the other relegated clubs, who were also the club against whom Albion had 50 per cent of their wins. Who were they?

736. On the opening day of that terrible season, West Brom drew 1-1 at home with Oxford United with a new signing from Sheffield Wednesday announcing his arrival with a goal. Who was he?

737. Albion didn't find playing at a lower level a whole lot easier in 1986-87, ending up in 15th place in the table. Only 7,127 were at Selhurst Park on 18 April 1987 to see Crystal Palace and WBA share the spoils in a 1-1 draw. Whose first goal for the club proved to be the first of many?

738. The 1987-88 season was Albion's worst to date, although something even more unpleasant was lurking round the corner. They survived in the Second Division by one point. There was just one hat-trick to savour and it came in a 3-2 home win over Huddersfield Town on 24 October 1987. Who scored it?

739. The 1988-89 season saw a rise to ninth, and when Albion beat Shrewsbury Town 4-0 at home on 2 January 1989, one of their goals was an own goal by a man who has been a Premier League manager now for over 20 years. Who was he?

740. The season of 1989-90 saw West Bromwich Albion back in the doldrums again when they equalled their terrible season of two years before, the only bright side being Don Goodman's goals. He got three when Albion excelled themselves on 11 November 1989 in a 7-0 win at the Hawthorns against a club they had once met in an FA Cup final. Who were they?

741. At the start of the new decade, Albion finally got out of the Second Division, but not how they had hoped, going down instead of up to experience third-level football for the first time in their history. Their top scorer in that 1990-91 season was something that assists you in going downstairs, and that seemed appropriate. Who was he?

742. They may not have liked playing at that level for the first time, but Albion certainly announced themselves at the Hawthorns on 17 August 1991 with a resounding 6-3 victory against which club who had travelled a long way to play them?

743. After a poor end to that 1991-92 season denied them a play-off place, West Brom got one the following season and made the most of it. It is of interest to note that they had been in Division Three in 1991-92, didn't get promoted but found they were then in Division Two and therefore upon going up were now in Division One – but not, of course, the Division One known to all. The hubristic so-called Premier League had arrived and rendered all statistics meaningless! The side that went up contained the most best-known literary surnames in the country. Who were the two players?

744. Bob Taylor was the runaway top scorer in that promoted side, but the only hat-trick came from another player in a 3-1 win over Brighton at the Hawthorns on 3 April 1993. Who scored it?

745. In 1993-94 it was only goal difference that kept Albion in their newly achieved second level of English football, but fans would have been pleased about the club that had been relegated instead of them. Who was it?

746. Which signing from Preston North End came up with a Hawthorns hat-trick when Albion beat Tranmere Rovers 5-1 on 30 April 1995?

747. On 7 September 1996, a player signed from neighbours Birmingham City opened his goalscoring account for West Bromwich Albion when they won 2-0 against QPR at Loftus Road. Who was he?

748. The 1997-98 season brought a fifth term at the second level and Albion's highest-placed finish of tenth. Another signing from Preston North End scored in their 2-1 home win over Tranmere Rovers on 9 August 1997. Who was he?

749. Interest was stirred by a new kid on the block who had the advantage of being a local lad as well. He announced his arrival with two of the three goals in a 3-2 win at Gresty Road against Crewe Alexandra on 16 August 1997. Who was he?

750. West Brom ended their worst decade in the Football League when they escaped by one place a drop back to the third level in 1999-2000. It was the first time in any season outside the top flight that they had scored less than a goal a game in the League – true or false?

751. When Albion won successive home games against Gillingham and Preston North End on 18 and 25 November 2000, one player scored all six goals. Who was he?

752. West Brom reached the play-offs but couldn't progress past the semi-final stage. Which three clubs, two from Lancashire and one from just down the road, also reached the play-offs?

753. The domestic cup competitions were a big disappointment with Albion being knocked out of both by the same club. Which one?

754. West Brom beat just one club in those cup competitions and did so 2-1 on aggregate against their first League Cup opponents. Who were they?
A. Cardiff City B. Newport County C. Swansea City D. Wrexham

755. Who bagged both goals when Albion won 2-1 against Sheffield Wednesday at Hillsborough on 8 October 2000?

756. Who was the only West Bromwich Albion player to start 45 of their 46 League outings?

757. Who scored his last Albion goal in a 2-2 draw with Crystal Palace at Selhurst Park on 3 February 2001, before joining Stockport County?

758. Whose two League goals that season came in home wins, by 2-1 and 3-1 against London clubs QPR and Wimbledon?

759. Jason Roberts scored his first goal for the club on 23 September 2000, and it proved to be the only goal of the game away to which southern club?

760. The first day of 2001 saw the last time that football was played in front of Albion's Rainbow Stand. They won 1-0 that day courtesy of an own goal – against which Yorkshire club?

761. Under Gary Megson's leadership, the latter stages of this 2001-02 season produced a dizzying promotion to the Premier League when it had looked for all the world as if the play-offs would be the best Albion could hope for. And the cherry on the icing on the cake was that Wolves had been odds-on to go up and didn't! The success was built from the back, with Albion conceding fewer goals than in any other 42-match League programme in their history. How many?

762. Up front Albion missed Jason Roberts, who was sidelined with injury for two thirds of the season. It is rare for a promoted club's top scorer to get just ten league goals, but their 24 clean sheets at the other end more than made up for the goal drought. Who was the club's top scorer with those ten goals, seven of which came in September?

763. Albion's late run produced seven wins in their last eight games, the only one they failed to win coming in a 1-1 draw in Yorkshire on 7 April 2002 – against which club?
A. Barnsley B. Bradford City C. Rotherham United D. Sheffield United

764. Promotion was clinched at the Hawthorns on 21 April 2002, when 26,701 saw Albion beat which London club 2-0 to cement the runners-up spot behind Manchester City?

765. Two other London clubs put paid to Albion's cup hopes, both winning 1-0 at the Hawthorns, in the quarter-final of the FA Cup and the third round of the League Cup. Who were they?

766. Earlier, Albion had knocked out two teams beginning with S, one from the FA Cup and the other from the League Cup. Who were they?

767. Who was voted the Baggies' player of the year?
A. Neil Clement B. Danny Dichio C. Russell Hoult D. Darren Moore

768. Whose penalties in both the third and fourth rounds of West Bromwich Albion's FA Cup run to the quarter-finals were vital to their progress?

769. On 16 February 2002, a team that at the season's end would be promoted from the fourth tier went to the Hawthorns for an FA Cup fifth round tie, going down narrowly to a Danny Dichio goal. Who were they?

770. The season's biggest League win came on 23 February 2002, when Albion won 5-0 at the Hawthorns against the club from which stalwart central defender Darren Moore had joined them. Who were they?

771. Although the heads of the players and the fans never dropped, Albion's first experience of the Premier League was a chastening affair. As they had been only the 12th highest goalscorers in gaining promotion, it was obvious that goals at the top level were going to be hard to come by. They managed just 29 in 38 games and started with a blank in a 1-0 defeat on the first Premier League ground on which they played, on 17 August 2002. Where?

772. Russell Hoult missed just one League game in goal but who was the only outfield player to start 36 of the 38?

773. Who, on 24 August 2002, with a 90th-minute consolation goal in a 3-1 home defeat to Leeds United, scored Albion's first ever Premier League goal?
A. Danny Dichio B. Scott Dobie C. Lee Marshall D. Jason Roberts

774. West Brom's first Premier League win came on the last day of August, when a Darren Moore goal gave them a 1-0 win over which London club?

775. Albion were eliminated from both domestic cup competitions by teams starting with W. Which two clubs beat them?

776. The club's only success in a cup tie came in the FA Cup third round, when they won 3-1 at home to a Yorkshire club. Which one?
A. Bradford City B. Doncaster Rovers C. Huddersfield Town D. Sheffield Wednesday

777. Who scored a hat-trick in that game?

778. Which midfielder was West Brom's player of the year?

779. Which player who was shortly to join the Albion scored a 90th-minute winner against them for Birmingham City at St Andrew's on 22 March 2003?

780. Danny Dichio and Scott Dobie ended up as joint top West Brom scorers in the League as the club were relegated with Sunderland and West Ham United. How many did each of them score?

781.   After a shock 4-1 defeat at neighbouring Walsall in their first match back at the second level, Albion responded with five wins in a row and Gary Megson's side achieved another promotion back to the big time, and if they hadn't lost their last three games, they might have gone up as champions. Which club did have that honour?

782.   Against which London club did West Brom come from three goals down to win 4-3 away from home on 8 November 2003?

783.   Albion's winning goal when they won 1-0 away to Derby County on 30 August 2003 came from someone who would later go on to play for the Rams. Who was he?

784.   Despite winning promotion, West Bromwich Albion had just one of their players represented in the PFA Division One team of the year. Who was he?

785.   West Brom's participation in the FA Cup lasted just one game: they went down 1-0 to another Midlands club away from home. Which one was it? A. Aston Villa B. Leicester City C. Nottingham Forest D. Wolves

786.   In the League Cup, Albion started out by beating one London club 4-0 at home and, after a good run, they lost 2-0 on the same ground to another London club in the quarter-final. Which two teams were involved?

787.   Although the highlight of that League Cup run was a 2-0 win against Manchester United on 3 December 2003, West Brom had made two visits to the north-east before that game, winning 2-1 on both occasions. Which two clubs did they beat?

788.   Which three men with surnames beginning with H found the net for West Brom in their League Cup exploits in 2003-04?

789.   Albion's player of the year was also the only man to start 45 of their 46 League games. Who was he?

790.   Who ended up as the club's top League goalscorer with 11 to his name?

791. On the morning of 15 May 2005, the season's last day, I walked into a betting shop and had £10 on West Brom to stay up at 6-1. They won, other results went their way and they became the first club to survive after being bottom at Christmas. Which club did they beat 2-0 that afternoon?

792. Why did the visiting club's fans join in the wild celebrations produced by their own team's defeat?

793. Albion's top Premier League goalscorer got their only League hat-trick and also came off the bench 13 times — way more than any other player. Who was he?

794. He picked up that hat-trick in the capital on 19 March 2005, when West Bromwich Albion had their only away win of the season by 4-1 — against which club?

795. Which club from the third level of English football who share Albion's colours knocked them out of the League Cup 2-1 after extra time in the first match of the competition on 21 September 2004?

796. Which West Brom defender came up with a very welcome 90th-minute equaliser at Aston Villa to make the score 1-1 in the Premier League on 10 April 2005?

797. Albion faced two clubs who play in the same colours in the FA Cup, beating the first of them 2-0 away before losing 3-1 in a replay after a 1-1 draw with the other one. Who were the two clubs?

798. Who would have been more than usually pleased to get Albion's goal in the aforementioned 3-1 FA Cup defeat, and why?

799. Although he was only on the pitch 20 times for the club in the League, which player impressed the fans enough to be voted Albion's player of the year?

800. Which midfielder was the only Albion player to play in all 38 League games?

801.   Albion failed to hold on to the Premier League status they had clung to by their fingernails the previous season. It was small recompense that Birmingham City joined them on their downward journey, but Albion ended up with twice as many points as the other relegated club, who won just three of their 38 games. Who were they?

802.   As 2004-05, Albion contrived to win just once away from home all season. It was in Lancashire this time, by 1-0 on 15 January 2006. Which club did they beat?

803.   Which defender who was scoring for the only time that season got that solitary goal?

804.   Which Albion midfielder, as well as being the only man to be on the pitch for all 38 Premier League games, also won their player of the year award?

805.   Which player got their first four goals of the season in the first four matches but then never scored again?

806.   Who were the only two players to score from the penalty spot during the season – one in a 4-0 League win over Everton and the other in a 1-1 draw with Reading in the FA Cup third round?

807.   Albion went out of the FA Cup to Reading, losing 3-2 after extra time in the replay after the 1-1 draw mentioned above. Both West Brom goals came from a midfielder who didn't score again all season in any competition. Who was he?

808.   Albion did well against both north London clubs at the Hawthorns, beating Arsenal 2-1 in October and Spurs 2-0 in December. Who scored for the Baggies in both games?

809.   Albion were finished off by a terrible run when they failed to win any of their last 13 League matches. They won for the last time on 4 February 2006, by 2-0 at the Hawthorns with the goals coming from Kevin Campbell and Jonathan Greening. Whom did they beat?

810.   Who were the only cub to whom Albion lost three times in all competitions over the season?

811.   Bryan Robson was replaced as manager by Tony Mowbray and Albion reached the play-offs again, only to fail at the last hurdle. Their 81 goals proved to be a higher total than 90 other clubs in the pyramid. Which club scored 83?

812.   A new record was created concerning the number of times West Brom met Wolves in a season, and another in the number of wins Albion achieved against their old enemy in a single season. How many games did they play against each other and how many did West Brom win?

813.   Who was the club's leading Championship goalscorer, helping himself to 20 of those 81?

814.   In the FA Cup, West Brom beat one Yorkshire club 3-1 but went out to another after a replay in the fifth round. Who were the two clubs?

815.   It was a similar story in the League Cup but this time involving two London clubs. Albion beat a side from the capital first time up by 3-0 away from home, but finally went out 2-0 at home to another. Who were the two clubs?

816.   In that same competition, Albion's other game produced a 3-1 home win when they came from behind to beat Cheltenham Town. Two of their goals came from penalties. Which two players were successful with them?

817.   Who was the only West Bromwich Albion player to score for them in both domestic cup competitions?
A. Darren Carter B. Jonathan Greening C. Diomansy Kamara
D. Kevin Phillips

818.   Kevin Phillips was a natural goalscorer and it didn't take long for his value to be seen. By far the highest scoring rate of his nine-club career came during his time at West Brom. He got two hat-tricks in 2006-07, the first of them coming in a 5-1 away win on 14 October 2006 -- against which club?

819.   Phillips' other hat-trick came when Albion finished the season in fine style at the Hawthorns on 6 May 2007 with a 7-0 win over which Yorkshire club?

820.   Which defender enjoyed the best Championship appearances record in 2006-07, starting 42 of West Brom's 46 matches?

821. The 2007-08 season proved to be a great one for the Baggies: they were promoted as champions and reached the FA Cup semi-finals for the first time in over a quarter of a century. Two men were vital to their success, with one of them winning the manager of the year award and the other taking gongs as Albion's and the Championship's player of the year. Who were the two men?

822. Which midfielder was the only player to appear in all of West Brom's 46 Championship games?

823. West Bromwich Albion scored more goals than all of the other 91 league clubs, and had the most home wins and the most away wins of anyone in their division – true or false?

824. West Brom scored five goals in the Championship twice at the Hawthorns. On the second occasion, in late December, they accounted for Scunthorpe United by 5-0, but earlier, at the end of September, they dispatched London opposition 5-1. Who were they?

825. Which club did West Bromwich Albion beat away from home in both domestic cup competitions – 3-0 in the FA Cup and 2-0 in the League Cup?

826. Which three Albion players – one a defender, another a midfielder and the third a striker – made it into the PFA divisional team of the year?

827. Which Albion forward was the only man to score in four consecutive league games for the club, and was also the only man to register a hat-trick in an FA Cup tie?
A. Roman Bednár   B. Robert Koren   C. Ishmael Miller   D. Kevin Phillips

828. For the only time in their history, Albion scored five goals away from the Hawthorns in the FA Cup on two occasions: by 5-0 in the fifth round against a Midlands club and by 5-1 against opposition from the west of the country in the sixth round. Which two clubs did they beat?

829. That last win took West Bromwich Albion to an FA Cup semi-final, in which they were beaten by a goal from an ex-player. Who?

830. Which club who also play in stripes went up with West Brom to the Premier League, where the pair were eventually joined by Hull City, who went up via the play-offs?

831. Although he tried to play good football to the end, Tony Mowbray's West Bromwich Albion experienced their third relegation in seven seasons and he departed at the end of the season to manage which club?

832. Each time they are relegated from the Premier League, West Brom seem to win one away game, and they did so again this time on 27 September 2008, by 1-0 at which opponents' ground courtesy of a Jonas Olsson goal?

833. Albion's player of the year was also their leading Premier League goalscorer with nine to his name. Who was he?

834. After getting past Peterborough United in the FA Cup third round, West Bromwich Albion succumbed to which Lancastrian opponents 3-1 after a 2-2 draw at the Hawthorns?

835. Albion's lone goal that night was scored by only the second player with a surname starting with Z to play for the club. Who was he?

836. West Brom also lost 3-1, this time after extra time, in the League Cup, in an away tie in the north-east. Which club beat them?

837. Who was the only man to score for Albion in both domestic cup competitions?

838. Which London club were holding West Bromwich Albion 0-0 at the Hawthorns on 28 December 2008 when goals in the 83rd and 94th minutes by the two Bs – Bednár and Beattie – ruined their day?

839. Albion finished bottom despite winning more games than the two clubs who went down with them. They weren't a million miles apart from each other geographically. Who were the two clubs?

840. At the start of this disappointing season a lot of work was done to improve a stand that was renamed the West Stand. What had it previously been called?

841. Yet again, Albion proved too good for the Championship as they gained another promotion under new man Roberto Di Matteo. Which club had he managed before taking over at West Brom?

842. In how many of their last nine seasons had Albion now experienced promotion or relegation?

843. West Bromwich Albion finished as runners-up to a side they knocked out of the FA Cup, winning 4-2 at the Hawthorns in the fourth round on 23 January 2010. Who were they?

844. Which Albion defender started in 43 of their 46 Championship matches?

845. Who was the only West Bromwich Albion player to be selected for the PFA divisional team of the year, and become the club's player of the year into the bargain?

846. Albion knocked Yorkshire opposition out of both domestic cup competitions. In the FA Cup it was by 2-0 away from home in the third round, while in the League Cup it was with a 4-3 home win in the second round. Which two clubs fell by the wayside?

847. Two southern clubs eventually put paid to Albion's progress in both competitions: one from London in the League Cup and the other about 30 miles west of the capital in the FA Cup. Who were the two clubs?

848. Only one other club of the 92 could match Albion's 41 goals on their travels in the Championship, scoring the same number. They were champions of the division below Albion. Who were they?

849. Only one player scored for the club in both domestic cup competitions. Who was it?

850. The Baggies recorded two 5-0 wins in the Championship at the Hawthorns: the first against Middlesbrough in September and the second the following month against Watford. What was unusual about those two games?

WBA SEASON 2010-2011

851. Having got up, this time Albion stayed there! It looked like being the same old story when they lost their first game 6-0, but when it came to the end of the season West Brom had attained their highest ever Premier League position. To whom did they lose 6-0 and what was their final League position?

852. Albion made another managerial change after Christmas when they looked to be on a downward spiral. Whom did they appoint and which club had recently dispensed with his services?

853. Which club knocked West Bromwich Albion out of the FA Cup for the third time in six seasons?

854. Albion enjoyed a decent run in the League Cup before going out at Ipswich. They won 2-0 and 4-1 away to two clubs beginning with L. Who were they?

855. Talking of clubs beginning with L brings us to a fine 2-1 League win over Liverpool at the Hawthorns on 2 April 2011. One man scored both goals that day. Who was he and in what way did the goals arrive?

856. Which midfielder who played in 33 of the club's 38 League games was voted Albion's player of the year?

857. Who became flavour of the month when he got a 90th-minute leveller at home to Wolves that made it 1-1 on 20 February 2011, and then repeated the trick to produce the same scoreline at Stoke City the following week, this time in the 87th minute?

858. Which Albion defender put through his own net twice during the season, once in the League and once in the League Cup, in neither instance doing any damage as West Bromwich Albion won both games, by 3-2 and 4-1?

859. Who was the Baggies' top League goalscorer with 15 to his name?

860. Although they were in no danger, Albion battled right to the end of the season, coming back on the final day, 22 May 2011, from a 3-0 deficit to draw 3-3 away to Newcastle United. Who scored all three of those comeback goals?

WBA SEASON 2011-2012

861. It's not very often that a team loses four more games than it wins and loses this number of home games yet finishes in the top half of the table, but West Brom managed to do so in 2011-12, breaking the previous year's record for their best ever Premier League position in finishing tenth. How many home games did they lose?

862. In fact, Albion lost the first and last home games of the season, the first courtesy of an 81st-minute own goal and the last due to terrible goalkeeping. Which two sides won 2-1 and 3-2 at the Hawthorns and which Albion player was the unfortunate 'own goal' man?

863. One reason that it was a good season was the fact that Albion topped the mini-league of the four West Midlands clubs for the first time since which season?

864. Albion went out of the FA Cup in the fourth round at home to Norwich City, but previously they had beaten Cardiff City 4-2 in the third round. Which player scored a hat-trick that day and which ex-Albion man scored for the visitors?

865. In the League Cup, West Bromwich Albion won 4-1 on the south coast before going out after extra time on Merseyside. Which two clubs did they play?

866. Which central defender was voted Albion's player of the year?

867. Against which club did West Bromwich Albion take a 2-0 lead after five minutes, through goals by James Morrison and Shane Long, only to end up drawing the game 2-2 away from home on the first day of October 2011?

868. Which Albion player was absent for just one of their 38 Premier League fixtures?

869. Albion won 3-2 at Newcastle United on 21 December 2011. Nobody with a shorter name than the scorer of the home side's goals has found the net against Albion in their history. Who was he and who grabbed the Baggies' winner in the 85th minute?

870. When West Brom beat Blackburn Rovers 3-0 at the Hawthorns on 7 April 2012, the same surname appeared on both sides. The Blackburn man contributed one of Albion's three goals. Who were the two players, who also represent the same country?

871. Under Steve Clarke this time, Albion topped their best ever Premier League position for the third year running in finishing eighth. In what position did they sit a third of the way through the season, after 13 matches?

872. Romelu Lukaku, on loan from Chelsea, was a real handful for defences and scored more than double the total of his nearest challengers in the Premier League scoring stakes at West Brom. How many goals did he get?

873. Who was the only Baggies player to score in both domestic cup competitions?

874. Which club from west London knocked Albion out of the FA Cup after a replay?
A. Brentford B. Chelsea C. Fulham D. QPR

875. Despite going out to Liverpool at home at the next hurdle, Albion won 4-2 away in the West Country in their opening League Cup tie. Whom did they beat?

876. After the Albion's best start to a season after seven games since winning the Division One title in 1919-20, it was a major disappointment to lose their next game 2-1 at home when playing against ten men for nearly 70 minutes and leading 1-0 with nine minutes left. Which club excelled themselves to win that day on 20 October 2012?

877. Despite scoring own goals at both Old Trafford and Carrow Road, which player who missed just two League games won the vote for Albion's player of the year?

878. West Brom won four League matches in a row against Southampton, Wigan Athletic, Chelsea and Sunderland. In which decade had they last won four successive league games in the top flight?
A. the 1970s B. the 1980s C. the 1990s D. the 2000s

879. They also reached 49 points, their best Premier League total yet, and won more games than in any other season in which they played Premier League football. How many did they win?

880. Albion's final game of the season was a special affair because it was Sir Alex Ferguson's last game in management. (a) What was the score with ten minutes to go? (b) What was the final score? (c) Who scored a hat-trick for Albion? (d) Which Albion player was unfortunate enough to score for Manchester United?

881.　It's usually a bad sign if your goalkeeper wins the player of the year award and, after three decent seasons in the top flight, Albion escaped relegation by one place after finishing 17th. Which keeper won the award?

882.　London clubs put Albion out of both domestic cup competitions. Which two were responsible?
A. Arsenal and Spurs　B. Arsenal and Crystal Palace
C. Spurs and West Ham United　D. West Ham United and Crystal Palace

883.　The Baggies' only win in a cup competition came when they beat a Welsh club 3-0 at the Hawthorns in the second round of the League Cup on 27 August 2013. Who were their opponents and which Albion forward got all three goals?

884.　Which West Brom defender came up with a 92nd-minute equaliser in a 1-1 draw against Fulham at Craven Cottage on 14 September 2013?

885.　Against which London club on 12 April 2014 did Albion roar into a 3-0 lead in the first half-hour, before allowing them to leave the Hawthorns with a point from a 3-3 draw after a goal in the 94th minute?

886.　In the previous season he had scored for Sunderland against West Bromwich Albion in both Premier League games, but his stripes had changed colour and he scored for Albion against his old club in a 3-0 win at the Hawthorns on 21 September 2013. Who was he?

887.　Referee Andre Marriner was a busy man when Albion visited Stamford Bridge on 9 November 2013 and came away with a 2-2 draw. He showed yellow cards to ten players. How many of the ten were wearing West Brom shirts?

888.　Which ex-Baggie found the net against his old club when West Bromwich Albion lost 2-0 at Hull City on 22 March 2014?

889.　Which Swiss city scored for Albion in their 1-1 home draw with Everton on 20 January 2014?

890.　Three players with surnames starting with A scored for West Brom in the Premier League during the 2013-14 season. I would imagine the club were pleased to see the back of one of them in particular! Who were the three?

891. West Brom survived another season at the top table, but not without another managerial upheaval at the end of December that steadied the defence and saw the team end up in 13th place. Who left and who replaced him?

892. Which ex-Albion player took just two minutes to put Everton ahead when they won 2-0 at the Hawthorns on 13 September 2014?

893. Which midfielder endeared himself to the home fans with a 72nd-minute winner against Aston Villa in a game Albion won 1-0 on 13 December 2014?

894. Which non-League club from the north-east did West Bromwich Albion clobber 7-0 in the FA Cup third round at the Hawthorns on 3 January 2015?

895. Albion were in London on 20 December 2014 and led 2-0 before going down 3-2, reminding older fans of a similar debacle in an important game nearly half a century before. Which club beat them?

896. It was quite a season for one player, who was the club's top Premier League scorer, the only man to appear in every League game and the scorer of four of the seven goals mentioned in question four. Who was he?

897. However, all that effort failed to win him Albion's player of the year award, which went to a defender instead. Which one?

898. Albion had a 1-0 away win over Manchester United at Old Trafford on 2 May 2015. Which defender scored their winning goal in the 63rd minute?

899. West Brom got over the line at Old Trafford when which goalkeeper saved which United player's penalty kick?

900. Albion went out of the League Cup at Bournemouth, but in the FA Cup, after their third round win, a victory by 4-0 over a London club was sandwiched between two short trips to play local rivals. Who were their three opponents, the last of which ended their run in the quarter-finals?

901. West Brom finished 14th in their sixth consecutive season of Premier League football, and for the first time since the last century more than one player started all 38 League games. Which two did so?

902. Most teams getting 34 goals from their 38 games end up relegated, but Tony Pulis had the defence well drilled to counteract the lack of punch up front. Albion's leading goalscorer ended up with nine goals. Who was he?

903. As we shall see later, it was vital that defenders chipped in with the odd goal, and it was a defender who was voted the Baggies' player of the year. Who was he?

904. On 16 April 2016, Watford went to the Hawthorns and won 1-0. Which Albion player had two penalties saved and who saved them?

905. That same bogey club that had already put Albion out of the FA Cup three times in recent years did so again, winning 3-1 in the fifth round. On that occasion, and in the third round, WBA journeyed south to play teams from the south-west and the south-east of the country in that order, winning after a replay on the first occasion. Which two clubs did they visit?

906. Which club knocked Albion out of the League Cup?
A. Newcastle United B. Northampton Town C. Norwich City
D. Nottingham Forest

907. When Albion played in the Premier League on 29 August 2015, it shouldn't have been too much of a struggle to win because the home side were reduced to nine men with an hour still to play. West Bromwich Albion squeezed through 1-0 against which opponents?

908. Which two defenders got the vital goals that allowed West Brom to leave Anfield with a point from a 2-2 draw with Liverpool on 13 December 2015?

909. It was also a defender who came up with a 90th-minute winner when Stoke City were beaten at the Hawthorns on 2 January 2016. Whose goal produced a 2-1 win?

910. Craig Dawson was so keen to get on the scoresheet that he scored for both sides when Albion drew 1-1 in London on 25 April 2016. Who were they playing?

911. West Bromwich Albion were back in the top half of the Premier League in 2016-17, but you could get some idea of how lopsided the League was when tenth-place Albion lost five more games than they won. Their player of the year was the only man to appear in all 38 of their League fixtures. Who was he?

912. Albion made a fair few League substitutions. Three players went on as substitutes on a total of 59 occasions. James Morrison came off the bench 14 times and James McClean had 21 sub appearances to his name, but which Albion man headed the list with 24?

913. West Brom were defeated by Everton 2-1 at the Hawthorns and 3-0 at Goodison Park. In the home game on 20 August 2016, a player who would eventually join the Baggies scored Everton's winner and, when the teams met again on Merseyside on 11 March 2017, an ex-Albion man scored one of Everton's goals. Who were the two men?

914. When Albion drew 1-1 at home to Spurs on 15 October 2016, which recent signing from that club scored West Brom's goal?

915. Salomón Rondón was Albion's top Premier League goalscorer and registered a hat-trick in their 3-1 home win over which club on 14 December 2016?

916. On the final day of 2016, West Brom won 2-1 away at Southampton with goals from Matt Phillips and Hal Robson-Kanu. Saints' goal came from an ex-Baggie and another Saints player received a red card in the last minute. Who were the two players?

917. On 14 January 2017 Albion lost 4-0 away to Spurs, while on 11 February 2017 they drew 2-2 at home to another London club in West Ham United. One player had contrasting fortunes, scoring an own goal in the first game and grabbing a 94th-minute leveller for West Brom in the second game. Still not satisfied, he got the winner against Bournemouth a fortnight later. Who was he?

918. Which Midlands club ensured that Albion's FA Cup 'run' lasted just one match when they won 2-1 at the Hawthorns in the third round?

919. It's not every day that a defender scores twice in a game, but Craig Dawson did so in a 3-1 home win over which club on 18 March 2017?

920. What was the significance of the goal scored by visiting player Michy Batshuayi at the Hawthorns on 12 May 2017?

921.   This time Albion's poor goalscoring record finally caught up with them, their total of 31 goals from 38 games not being good enough to preserve their Premier League place. Which two players with surnames beginning with the same letter topped their scoring chart in the League with seven apiece?

922.   The man who scored the season's first Albion goal in the Premier League, in a 1-0 win over Bournemouth on 12 August 2017, was also the only player to start all 38 League games. Who was he?

923.   Which manager was sacked after his fourth defeat in a row on 18 November 2017, by 4-0 at home to Chelsea?

924.   His replacement, Alan Pardew, found the job even harder and managed to win just one of his 20 games in charge. It came in a 2-0 win at the Hawthorns on 13 January 2018 – against which club?

925.   How many games in succession did Albion lose under Pardew before they pulled the plug on him on 2 April 2018?

926.   In the FA Cup Albion won their first game 2-0 in Devon, while in the League Cup they won 3-1 first time out in Lancashire. Which two clubs did they eliminate from those competitions?

927.   Which club went to the Hawthorns twice in February 2018, beating Albion 3-2 on an afternoon when the life of Cyrille Regis was honoured, and then returning a fortnight later to knock West Brom out of the FA Cup?

928.   When Arsenal visited the Hawthorns on the last day of 2017 and drew 1-1 with Albion, an own goal by the home side put the away side in front with seven minutes to go, but Albion equalised from the penalty spot after 89 minutes. Who were responsible for the own goal and the spot kick that cancelled it out?

929.   Which ex-Spur scored Albion's 92nd-minute winner against his old club when West Brom beat them 1-0 on 5 May 2018?

930.   Darren Moore took over the reins in a caretaker capacity to the end of the season. Although Albion lost the last game of the season and were relegated, he won a manager of the month award and was unbeaten in his first how many games in charge?

931. Albion reached the play-offs in their first season of Championship football for the best part of a decade, going down at the semi-final stage. They weren't helped by having a player sent off in each game. Who were the two players?

932. In the League Cup, West Brom were drawn at home to two Towns, beating them by 1-0 and 2-1. Who were they?

933. They eventually went out of both domestic cup competitions in the fourth round, to two clubs who dislike each other intensely in a rivalry that has been dubbed the A23 derby. Who are they?

934. Which 'new kid on the block' scored nine times in 26 Championship outings and looked as if he had been playing at that level for years?

935. Dwight Gayle was Albion's top league goalscorer with 23 to his name, and registered hat-tricks in a 4-0 win in Yorkshire and a 4-1 home win against a Lancastrian club. Which two clubs were involved?

936. Gayle's 'top goalscorer' accolade was a close-run thing because he landed it by just one goal – from which man?

937. On 18 August, Albion recorded the biggest win of the season in the Championship when they beat which club 7-1 at the Hawthorns?

938. Which player appeared in all 46 Championship games for West Brom?

939. If you take the last letter away from one of the scorers when Albion won 2-1 at Sheffield United on 14 December 2018, the two of them produce a Bee Gee. Who scored the goals?

940. The decision to sack Darren Moore after a 1-1 draw with Ipswich Town left a bad taste in a number of mouths as well as mine. Since taking the job he had won twice as many games as he had lost. Who took over as caretaker manager until the end of the season?

941. Slaven Bilić got Albion automatic promotion back into the Premier League after two years' absence. At one point they won six games in a row and tasted defeat just once before Christmas, by 1-0 on the first day of October – against which club?

942. Which Albion player turned things round with two second-half goals when they went in at the interval trailing 1-0 to Luton Town at Kenilworth Road on 17 August 2019?

943. Inside three days in August 2019, Albion drew 1-1 at home with Reading and 1-1 away to Derby County. On both occasions they were saved by a late penalty taken by the same player. Who was he?

944. Later in the season, in November and December, a similar thing happened, except at home to Sheffield Wednesday and away to Preston North End. The two late penalties were winning goals in 2-1 and 1-0 wins, and someone else took the spot kicks. Who was he?

945. Which Yorkshire club received a total of eight yellow cards when they visited the Hawthorns and drew 2-2 on 22 October 2019?

946. Which Albion player began the new year on 1 January 2020 by scoring for both West Brom and Leeds United when the teams drew 1-1 at the Hawthorns?

947. Charlie Austin and Hal Robson-Kanu shared the top Championship goalscorer honours for West Brom with ten each, but the really amazing fact was the number of Albion players who scored for them in the league in 2019-20. How many was it?
A. 16 B. 17 C. 18 D. 19

948. Albion went out of the FA Cup 3-2 at home to Newcastle United in the fifth round, but all their other three opponents in the two domestic cup competitions came from London. They won 1-0 against two of them in the third and fourth rounds of the FA Cup and lost 2-1 at home to the other in the League Cup. Who were the three clubs?

949. Which West Brom man missed none of the 46 Championship matches, and which midfielder was the club's player of the year?

950. Which club would have had automatic promotion and been runners-up to Leeds United, denying Albion in the process, if they had beaten Barnsley on the last day of the extended, Covid-ridden season instead of losing 2-1 at home while Albion were drawing 2-2 with QPR at the Hawthorns?

951. After gaining promotion, Albion struggled in the rarefied air of the Premier League, and Slaven Bilić was shown the door after one win in their first 13 games. It came against a team that were relegated with them. Who were they, and which other club went down?

952. The season's craziest score came when Albion visited the capital on 3 April 2021 with everyone expecting a heavy defeat on a ground on which they had last won over 40 years before. By what score did they win and whom did they beat?

953. The man who turned the game around that day, with two goals in added-on time at the end of the first half, was also the club's leading Premier League goalscorer with 11 to his name. Who was he?

954. The size of the task facing Sam Allardyce when he became Albion's new manager on 20 December 2020 became obvious when they lost 3-0 at home to give Baggies fans a terrible Christmas. Who beat them, and which West Brom player didn't help matters when he received a red card after 36 minutes?

955. Albion took creditable points away from home by drawing 1-1 at both Liverpool and Manchester United. Their Anfield goal came after 82 minutes, while the one at Old Trafford gave them a second-minute lead. Which two players scored those goals?

956. West Brom's player of the year was not a surprise. He was also the only Albion man to miss just one League game. Who was he?

957. Just how far out of their depth West Bromwich Albion were was evidenced by the fact that in the space of 28 days in December and January they lost 5-0 at home twice and 4-0 – to which three clubs?

958. Albion went out of both domestic cup competitions on penalties, to clubs that began with the same letter. Who were they? Note the continued devaluation of the FA Cup, with no replays in the picture!

959. Which new arrivals in the Football League did Albion beat 3-0 in their first League Cup game of the season?

960. Although Albion were relegated, they asked Sam Allardyce if he wanted to stay and, after he had declined the offer, they turned to someone who had made a mark by taking an unfancied side to the Championship play-offs. Who was he and with which club did he overachieve?

961. A season that started promisingly fell apart in the new year and saw Albion in tenth place at the end. They had been in the top four of the Championship all the way to the 25th game of the season, when the only question appeared to be whether it would be automatic promotion or the play-offs. In which number game did they lose for the first time, on 1 October, and who beat them 1-0?

962. Which surname scored for Albion at Bournemouth on the opening day and in the first home game against Luton Town, and then scored an own goal for Albion when Sheffield United were beaten 4-0 at the Hawthorns in the season's third match?

963. In successive weeks in August, the Baggies won 2-1 away at Blackburn Rovers and 1-0 at Peterborough United. In the first encounter they scored in the first minute, while in the second they won the game in the 94th minute. Which two players came up with those early and late strikes?

964. West Brom didn't last very long in the FA Cup, going out in the third round by 2-1 after extra time at home to which Premier League side?

965. The League Cup proved to be very painful indeed when Arsenal went to the Hawthorns and returned to London having won by what scoreline?

966. Which player did the double by making the most Championship appearances and scoring the most goals for Albion?

967. Albion were live on the box on 11 March 2022, by which time the steam had gone from their season. The opposite was happening to their visitors, Huddersfield Town, who sailed into a two-goal lead. However, for those Baggies fans who hadn't gone home early, Albion bounced back to grab a point with an 84th-minute penalty and an equaliser a minute later. Which two players scored?

968. On 17 December 2021, Albion drew 0-0 at Barnsley, while on 14 February 2022 they drew 0-0 at home to Blackburn Rovers. What links the two games?

969. On 2 January 2022 at the Hawthorns, three players were sent off in a game that ended 1-1. Albion produced two thirds of them in Sam Johnstone and Alex Mowatt. Who were they playing against?

970. When Albion prevailed 2-1 at Coventry City on 4 December 2021, one of the home club's players scored for both sides. Who was he?

971. Albion rescued what looked like being a terrible season to still have a chance of a play-off place on the last day. On 10 October the man in charge paid with his job for just one win in the opening 13 games. Who was he, and who were the only side they beat and by what score at the Hawthorns on 20 August?

972. Who held the fort for a fortnight, and who arrived to manage the club on 25 October?

973. The improvement was evident straight away as Albion went on a run of nine wins in ten matches, starting on the first day of November and lasting until the middle of January. The only club to lower their colours during this time did so by 1-0 on 21 December, in a game that didn't necessitate a long journey for Albion. Who beat them?

974. Albion's new signing from Millwall, Jed Wallace, announced himself with both goals in a 2-2 away draw with which club on 27 August?

975. In the League Cup, WBA met two sides who are geographically close to each other, winning against the first of them 1-0 at home through a Karlan Grant goal, and then exiting the competition in the next round via the second side, by the same score away from home. Which two teams did they come up against?

976. Grant was on the mark for Albion again in the FA Cup third round, when they were involved in a 3-3 thriller away from home before winning the Hawthorns replay 4-0. Who were their third round opponents and which player scored early and late, in the second and 93rd minutes of the first game?

977. West Brom won 2-0 away and then lost 2-0 at home in the Championship to the team that knocked them out in the next round of the FA Cup. Who were they?

978. Which player who had experienced some great times at Celtic scored his first Albion goal in a 2-1 win at Sunderland on 12 December?

979. Which ex-Albion man scored from the penalty spot against the Baggies in a 1-1 draw at the Hawthorns on 2 September, and who was he playing for?

980. The last day of the season was a crazy one, when Albion contrived to lose in the last minute after leading twice. Even if they had won they would not have reached the play-offs, because Sunderland had a better goal difference. Which club completed the double over Albion with the same 3-2 scoreline by which they had won won earlier in the season at the Hawthorns?

All of these players joined West Bromwich Albion from a non-British club. Which one was it in each instance?

981.   Fabian De Freitas – joined in 1998

982.   Brian Jensen – joined in 2000

983.   Peter Odemwingie – joined in 2010

984.   Nicolas Anelka – joined in 2013

985.   Salomón Rondón – joined in 2015

986.   Claudio Yacob – joined in 2012

987.   Cristian Gamboa – joined in 2014

988.   Youssouf Mulumbu – joined in 2009

989.   Markus Rosenberg – joined in 2012

990.   Filip Krovinović – joined on loan in 2019

991. In their final Football League game of the 1931-32 season, Albion lost at home to Grimsby Town, who were relegated that season, by a rare scoreline. Twenty-five years later, when they welcomed the Soviet Red Army side CDSA to the Hawthorns to celebrate the switching-on of their floodlights, they won by this same rare scoreline. What was it?

992. West Brom became the first western club to tour China in the summer of 1978, and there were some interesting aspects. Which Albion player, when asked if he would be visiting the Great Wall of China, replied: "When you've seen one wall, you've seen them all."

993. When England beat Switzerland 6-0 at Highbury on 2 December 1948, a West Brom player made his international debut and scored two of the goals. He was never picked again and therefore had a 200 per cent goalscoring record in an England shirt! Who was he?

994. Which two post-Second World War Albion managers have also been in charge of Birmingham City and Aston Villa?

995. Who was the last West Brom man to be the country's top Football League goalscorer, and in what season did it occur?

996. The score at the Hawthorns on 18 May 1982 was 2-0 to the Albion on the pitch, but the significant numbers off it were 50 people taken to hospital and 23 arrested. Who were in town?

997. Which gifted young Italian playmaker appeared in just 47 Football League games for West Bromwich Albion between 1998 and 2000, before the board took £4.25 million from Juventus and he returned to his birthplace?

998. Brendon Batson was a favourite of the crowd at the Hawthorns during an Albion career that was cut short by injury. He scored one Football League goal for the club in a 3-1 win over Ipswich Town on 4 April 1981, and one goal in the FA Cup, in a 4-0 win over Coventry City on 15 January 1979. He never scored for Albion without all their other goals on the day also being scored by players whose surnames began with B. Which three players scored the other five Albion goals in those two games?

999. Which two West Brom players, the first a defender who played in 104 Premier and Football League games for the club from 2001 to 2006, and the second a forward who turned out for them in 57 league games between 2008 and 2011, share the same surname?

1000. When Brian Talbot was sacked in January 1991, Stuart Pearson took over as caretaker manager for six games. What did those two men do as players that only one other West Brom manager has done, and who was that other manager?

THE WBA QUIZ BOOK ANSWERS

QUIZ NO 1 - ALBION'S EUROPEAN ADVENTURES

1. Every tie began with the away leg.
2. B – Bobby Hope.
3. Asa Hartford.
4. D – 3-1.
5. Tony Brown and Laurie Cunningham.
6. Dunfermline Athletic.
7. Fraser.
8. D – Ally Robertson.
9. Tony Brown.
10. Red Star Belgrade.

QUIZ NO 2 - ALBION V ASTON VILLA: CUP COMPETITIONS

11. Four Acres, the Oval, Crystal Palace, Molineux and St Andrew's.
12. Joe Carter.
13. Brian Whitehouse.
14. Arsenal v Liverpool, Arsenal v Chelsea, Chelsea v Manchester United and Arsenal v Newcastle United.
15. D – John Kaye.
16. Bobby Hope.
17. C – Astle and Suggett.
18. Derek Statham.
19. 1931.
20. 1924-25.

QUIZ NO 3 - ALBION V ASTON VILLA: LEAGUE

21. Tom Pearson.
22. A – Steve Hunt.
23. Scored League hat-tricks against Aston Villa.
24. 7-0.
25. Len Millard.
26. Tony Brown.
27. D – 16.
28. Fabian Delph.
29. Craig Dawson scored and Ahmed Hegazi and Mason Holgate missed theirs.
30. Dwight Gayle.

QUIZ NO 4 - ALBION V BIRMINGHAM CITY: CUP COMPETITIONS

31. 1955-56.
32. 0-0.
33. 1967-68.
34. Jeff Astle and Tony Brown.
35. West Brom won 2-1.
36. Victor Anichebe.
37. WG Richardson in the FA Cup final of 1930-31.
38. The League Cup in season 1984-85.
39. The Anglo-Italian Cup.
40. Paul Raven and Tony Rees.

QUIZ NO 5 - ALBION V BIRMINGHAM CITY: LEAGUE

41. A – Fred Buck.
42. D – Charlie Wilson.
43. Both matches ended 0-0.
44. 5-3, 6-0 and 7-1.
45. Derek Kevan.
46. C – Ken Foggo.
47. Carl Valentine and Imre Varadi.
48. 1991-92 and 2002-03.
49. 3-1.
50. Jake Livermore and Charlie Austin.

QUIZ NO 6 - ALBION V WOLVES: CUP COMPETITIONS

51. Wilson.
52. Won eight, drawn two, lost none.
53. Molineux, Stoney Lane and the Hawthorns.
54. Clive Clark.
55. 1888 and 1931.
56. 1930-31.
57. The sixth round.
58. Diomansy Kamara, Kevin Phillips and Zoltán Gera.
59. Green, Gregory and Griffin.
60. True.

QUIZ NO 7 - ALBION V WOLVES: LEAGUE

61. 8-0.
62. 7-3 to West Bromwich Albion.
63. D – Johnny Nicholls.
64. Derek Kevan.
65. Cyrille Regis.
66. Lee Hughes.
67. C – Jordão.
68. Kevin Phillips.
69. Peter Odemwingie.
70. Matheus Pereira.

QUIZ NO 8 - ANYTHING GOES

71. 1. Sheffield United.
72. D – Sunderland.
73. B – Tony Brown.
74. C – Spurs.
75. Juan Mata and Joël Matip.
76. Adrian Chiles and Frank Skinner.
77. It was the only season in which they won, drew and lost the same number of games – 14.
78. It cost more to produce stripes and such use of time and money was considered a luxury.
79. Preston North End.
80. As support for the 'Justice for Jeff' campaign.

QUIZ NO 9 - BIRTHPLACES

81. Leeds.
82. London.
83. Barnsley.
84. Manchester.
85. Eastwood.
86. Jimmy Dugdale – born in Liverpool.
87. Bristol.
88. Eddie Colquhoun.

89. Wolverhampton.

90. York, Doncaster and Wetherby.

QUIZ NO 10 - CHRISTMAS CRACKERS

91. B – Derby County.

92. C – Grimsby Town.

93. Cardiff City.

94. Elm Park, Reading.

95. A – Ray Barlow.

96. D – Preston North End.

97. Spurs.

98. Rob Green.

99. C – Hillsborough.

100. Middlesbrough, Manchester City, Birmingham City and Burnley.

QUIZ NO 11 - CRYPTIC ALBION PART 1

101. Ronnie Wallwork.

102. Paul Dyson.

103. Gary Bannister.

104. Alan Merrick.

105. Brian Whitehouse.

106. Carl Valentine.

107. Jimmy Dudley.

108. Alf Bentley.

109. Paddy Mulligan.

110. Peter Barnes.

QUIZ NO 12 - CRYPTIC ALBION PART 2

111. Dan Nurse.

112. Stacey North.

113. Gary Owen.

114. Bobby Cram.

115. Remi Moses.

116. Craig Shakespeare.

117. Derek Statham.

118. HJ Boston.

119. Kevin Donovan.

120. Matt Carbon.

QUIZ NO 13 - CUP FINAL MEN PART 1 BEFORE THE ALBION

121. Peter Hucker.

122. Peter Barnes.

123. Geoff Hurst.

124. Tony Grealish.

125. Gareth Barry.

126. Garth Crooks.

127. Giles.

128. Ken McNaught, Tony Morley, Kenny Swain and Nigel Spink.

129. Arthur Albiston.

130. John Deehan.

QUIZ NO 14 - CUP FINAL MEN PART 2 AFTER THE ALBION

131. Maurice Setters.

132. Cyrille Regis.

133. David Burrows.

134. Asa Hartford.

135. Danny Hegan.

136. Carlton Palmer.

137. Bryan Robson.

138. Danny Gabbidon.

139. Ugo Ehiogu.

140. David Cross.

QUIZ NO 15 - EDIBLE ALBION

141. Neil Parsley.
142. Michael Fudge.
143. Joe Mayo.
144. George McVitie.
145. Brian Rice.
146. Jack Crisp.
147. ER Fryer.
148. Billy Bassett.
149. Bobby Blood.
150. Harry Raw.

QUIZ NO 16 - FA CUP FINALS PART 1

151. Ten.
152. Preston North End.
153. True.
154. WG Richardson.
155. They have all appeared in three successive FA Cup finals.
156. Banks and Wilson.
157. Ronnie Allen.
158. Birmingham.
159. Blackburn Rovers and Barnsley.
160. Tufnell.

QUIZ NO 17 - FA CUP FINALS PART 2

161. Sheffield Wednesday, 4-2, in 1935.
162. Aston Villa.
163. Nicholls.
164. Jeff Astle.
165. Jim Sanders and Ray Barlow.
166. Frank Griffin.
167. Pearson.

168. Tommy Glidden, Len Millard and Graham Williams.
169. Jimmy Dugdale with Aston Villa.
170. Green, Bell and Richardson.

QUIZ NO 18 - FA CUP SEMI-FINALS

171. Preston North End.
172. Portsmouth and Nwankwo Kanu.
173. Spurs and QPR.
174. Jasper Geddes.
175. Tony Brown.
176. Birmingham.
177. Port Vale.
178. Small Heath.
179. Brian Whitehouse.
180. Ronnie Allen and Jeff Astle.

QUIZ NO 19 - FLORA, FAUNA, FISH AND FOWL

181. Paul Raven.
182. Ruel Fox.
183. Arthur Swift.
184. R Pike.
185. J Swallow.
186. Steve Bull.
187. Teddy Pheasant.
188. Fred Buck.
189. Bob Finch.
190. Sam Field.

QUIZ NO 20 - THE FOREIGN LEGION PART 1

191. Australia.
192. Grenada.
193. Nigeria.

194. Senegal.

195. Hungary.

196. Slovenia.

197. South Korea.

198. New Zealand.

199. Czech Republic.

200. Austria.

QUIZ NO 21 - THE FOREIGN LEGION PART 2

201. Chile.

202. Spain.

203. Slovakia.

204. Cameroon.

205. Romania.

206. Macedonia.

207. Burundi.

208. Sweden.

209. Belgium.

210. Egypt.

QUIZ NO 22 - GOALKEEPERS PART 1

211. Liverpool, Aston Villa and Bursaspor.

212. Nigel Spink.

213. Norman Heath.

214. Jim Cumbes.

215. Paul Barron and Paul Bradshaw.

216. Stuart Naylor.

217. John Osborne.

218. Joe Reader.

219. Tony Godden.

220. Ben Foster and Paul Robinson for Spurs against Watford.

QUIZ NO 23 - GOALKEEPERS PART 2

221. Tony Millington.

222. Russell Hoult.

223. Mark Grew.

224. Tomasz Kuszczak.

225. David Button.

226. He had Covid.

227. Boaz Myhill.

228. Bob Roberts.

229. Dean Kiely.

230. Alisson of Liverpool.

QUIZ NO 24 - HELPING HANDS 1946-2000

231. Ted Croker.

232. Alf Ramsey.

233. Tommy Docherty.

234. Jack Charlton.

235. Frank O'Farrell.

236. Maurice Setters.

237. Barry Kitchener.

238. Norman Hunter.

239. Chris Hughton.

240. Eric Nixon.

QUIZ NO 25 - HELPING HANDS 2000-2023

241. Shola Ameobi.

242. Dejan Stefanović.

243. Richard Dunne.

244. Patrice Evra.

245. Sylvain Distin.

246. Costel Pantilimon.

247. Esteban Cambiasso.

248. Winston Reid.

249. Rúben Dias.

250. Tyrone Mings.

QUIZ NO 26 - HOMES OF THE ALBION

251. A – the Birches.

252. B – Four Acres.

253. Noah's Ark.

254. Frank Heaven.

255. B – Derby County.

256. C – 'Chippy' Simmons.

257. Steve Bloomer.

258. B – Belgium.

259. A – Arsenal.

260. Aston Villa.

QUIZ NO 27 - INTERNATIONALS: ENGLAND (POST-WW2)

261. Don Howe.

262. Bryan Robson.

263. Ray Barlow and Tony Brown.

264. Five.

265. Johnny Nicholls.

266. Bobby Robson.

267. Derek Kevan.

268. Neither; he won three at each club.

269. Derek Statham.

270. True.

QUIZ NO 28 - INTERNATIONALS: NORTHERN IRELAND (POST-WW2)

271. Reg Ryan.

272. Dave Walsh.

273. Jack Vernon.

274. Gerry Armstrong.

275. Danny Hegan.

276. Chris Brunt.

277. Jonny Evans.

278. Chris Baird.

279. Gareth McAuley.

280. James Quinn.

QUIZ NO 29 - INTERNATIONALS: REPUBLIC OF IRELAND (POST-WW2)

281. Keith Andrews.

282. Tony Grealish.

283. Ray Treacy.

284. Paul McShane.

285. Kevin Kilbane.

286. Johnny Giles.

287. Simon Cox.

288. Shane Long.

289. James McClean.

290. Paddy Mulligan.

QUIZ NO 30 - INTERNATIONALS: SCOTLAND (POST-WW2)

291. Doug Fraser.

292. Bobby Hope.

293. Willie Johnston.

294. Scott Dobie.

295. Nigel Quashie.

296. Asa Hartford.

297. Darren Fletcher.

298. Graham Dorrans.

299. Derek McInnes.

300. James Morrison.

QUIZ NO 31 - INTERNATIONALS: WALES (POST-WW2)

301. Paul Mardon.
302. Graham Williams.
303. Andy Johnson.
304. Rob Earnshaw.
305. Jason Koumas.
306. Mickey Thomas.
307. Ronnie Rees.
308. Stuart Williams.
309. Dick Krzywicki.
310. James Chester.

QUIZ NO 32 - LEAGUE CUP FINALS

311. West Ham United.
312. QPR.
313. Mark Lazarus.
314. Manchester City.
315. Clive Clark.
316. Jeff Astle.
317. Geoff Hurst.
318. Asa Hartford.
319. Jimmy Hagan and Alan Ashman.
320. A – 11.

QUIZ NO 33 - MANAGERS PART 1

321. Stuart Pearson and Nigel Pearson.
322. Roy Hodgson and Sam Allardyce.
323. Managed West Bromwich Albion in two different centuries.
324. Fred Everiss.
325. Ronnie Allen, Roberto Di Matteo, Stuart Pearson and Brian Talbot.
326. Michael Appleton.

327. Ossie Ardiles and Nobby Stiles.
328. Bobby Gould.
329. Henry Ford – the managers were Henry Jackson and Louis Ford.
330. Roberto Di Matteo – Chelsea.

QUIZ NO 34 - MANAGERS PART 2

331. Archie Macaulay, Steve Clarke, Alan Irvine and Ron Wylie.
332. Ron Saunders.
333. Ron Atkinson and Keith Burkinshaw.
334. Vic Buckingham.
335. Pepe Mel.
336. Tony Mowbray in 2007-08.
337. Nobby Stiles.
338. Darren Moore.
339. Ossie Ardiles.
340. Valérien Ismaël.

QUIZ NO 35 - OPENING DAYS

341. C – Oldham Athletic.
342. Norwich City and Nottingham Forest.
343. D – Bill Foulkes.
344. Burnley.
345. Luton Town and Swansea Town.
346. A – Arsenal.
347. D – Sheffield Wednesday.
348. Spurs.
349. John Hartson and Hull City.
350. D – Glossop.

QUIZ NO 36 - OTHER COMPETITIONS

351. The Youth Cup.
352. Spurs and Arsenal.
353. D – Dick Krzywicki.
354. Ajax.
355. The Texaco Cup and the Watney Cup.
356. The Autoglass Trophy.
357. The Full Members' Cup, the Simod Cup and the Zenith Data Systems Cup.
358. St Mirren and Rangers.
359. D – Southampton.
360. A punch-up on the pitch.

QUIZ NO 37 - PENALTY SHOOT-OUTS

361. Cambridge United.
362. Middlesbrough.
363. Charlton Athletic.
364. Arsenal.
365. Oxford United.
366. Peterborough United.
367. Port Vale.
368. Northampton Town.
369. Blackpool.
370. Brentford.

QUIZ NO 38 - PLAY-OFFS

371. Swansea City.
372. Port Vale.
373. Andy Hunt.
374. Bolton Wanderers.
375. Wolves.
376. Derby County.
377. Paul Peschisolido.

378. Dean Kiely, Jason Koumas, Diomansy Kamara and Robert Koren.
379. 2018-19.
380. Kevin Phillips.

QUIZ NO 39 - POT LUCK

381. Steve Bull and Luther Blissett.
382. Craven Cottage.
383. C – 301.
384. Helmut Haller and Mario Kempes.
385. West Bromwich Strollers – they had to walk to Wednesbury to buy a football because there were none to be had in West Bromwich.
386. Sam Allardyce – one each time.
387. Joe Bradford.
388. Jimmy Cookson.
389. Colin Suggett and Kevin Kilbane.
390. Renton.

QUIZ NO 40 - RED CARDS

391. Derek McInnes.
392. Millwall and Hull City – Lions and Tigers.
393. Hal Robson-Kanu.
394. Jake Livermore.
395. West Ham United and Burnley.
396. Pablo Ibáñez and Jara.
397. Jay Rodriguez.
398. Manchester City.
399. Marc-Antoine Fortuné.
400. Peter Odemwingie, Goran Popov and Claudio Yacob.

QUIZ NO 41 - TRANSFERS 1888-1939

401. Alf Bentley – 9.
402. Bobby Blood – 4.
403. Jimmy Cookson – 1.
404. Stan Davies – 10.
405. Ben Garfield – 2.
406. Billy Garraty – 8.
407. Billy Light – 3.
408. Jack Mahon – 7.
409. Teddy Pheasant – 5.
410. Walter Robbins – 6.

QUIZ NO 42 - TRANSFERS 1946-1960

411. Derek Hogg.
412. Ray Potter.
413. Derek Kevan.
414. Maurice Setters.
415. David Burnside.
416. Frank Griffin.
417. George Lee.
418. Stan Rickaby.
419. Stuart Williams.
420. Jim Sanders.

QUIZ NO 43 - TRANSFERS 1960-1975

421. Ray Crawford.
422. Colin Suggett.
423. John Kaye.
424. Ronnie Fenton.
425. Clive Clark.
426. Ally Brown.
427. Allan Glover.
428. Eddie Colquhoun.
429. Ian Collard.
430. John Talbut.

QUIZ NO 44 - TRANSFERS 1975-1990

431. Brendon Batson.
432. Gary Thompson.
433. Tony Grealish.
434. Tony Ford.
435. David Mills.
436. Garth Crooks.
437. Imre Varadi.
438. Laurie Cunningham.
439. Paul Dyson.
440. Stephen MacKenzie.

QUIZ NO 45 - TRANSFERS 1990-2005

441. Kevin Kilbane.
442. Matt Carbon.
443. Paul Agnew.
444. Craig Shakespeare.
445. Kwame Ampadu.
446. Ian Hamilton.
447. Paul Holmes.
448. Peter Butler.
449. Kevin Donovan.
450. Sean Flynn.

QUIZ NO 46 - TRANSFERS 2005-2020

451. Curtis Davies.
452. Jonathan Greening.
453. Darren Fletcher.
454. Boaz Myhill.
455. Craig Dawson.
456. Steven Reid.
457. Abdoulaye Méïté.

458. Shane Long.

459. Nathan Ellington.

460. Richard Chaplow.

QUIZ NO 47 - 12 TOP THROSTLES NO 1: RONNIE ALLEN

461. Port Vale and Crystal Palace – he scored 34 for each club.

462. Wolves.

463. Five.

464. Scotland and West Germany.

465. Cardiff City.

466. Newcastle United.

467. 1954-55.

468. The Charity Shield – a 4-4 draw.

469. The Festival of Britain.

470. C – Bolton Wanderers.

QUIZ NO 48 - 12 TOP THROSTLES NO 2: JEFF ASTLE

471. Notts County and Leicester City.

472. John Kaye.

473. Charlie Wayman and Peter Osgood.

474. B – Hampden Park.

475. 1969-70.

476. Wolves.

477. Coventry City and West Ham United.

478. Northampton Town.

479. D – Sheffield.

480. Bristol City and South Africa.

QUIZ NO 49 - 12 TOP THROSTLES NO 3: BILLY BASSETT

481. Aston Villa.

482. Wolves.

483. B – Derby County.

484. Southshore.

485. Scotland.

486. Darwen.

487. D – the Victoria Ground.

488. Molineux.

489. Chairman.

490. The FA Cup semi-final against Preston North End.

QUIZ NO 50 - 12 TOP THROSTLES NO 4: TONY BROWN

491. Ipswich Town.

492. Wales.

493. 1970-71.

494. He was born in Oldham.

495. C – Nottingham.

496. Peterborough United.

497. Manchester United.

498. Spurs.

499. Coventry City and West Ham United.

500. Carlisle United and Torquay United.

QUIZ NO 51 - 12 TOP THROSTLES NO 5: TOMMY GLIDDEN

501. B – Goodison Park.

502. C – Sheffield United.

503. In the semi-final against Everton.

504. Joe Carter.

505. Jimmy Cookson.

506. West Ham United and Burnley.

507. 1931-32 and 1933-34.

508. Swansea Town.

509. Blackpool.

510. Coach and director.

QUIZ NO 52 - 12 TOP THROSTLES NO 6: DEREK KEVAN

511. Everton.

512. A – Highbury.

513. Scotland.

514. 1961-62.

515. Ipswich Town.

516. B – Mexico.

517. A – Plymouth Argyle.

518. Birmingham City and Blackpool.

519. Fulham and Bolton Wanderers.

520. Manchester City.

QUIZ NO 53 - 12 TOP THROSTLES NO 7: CYRILLE REGIS

521. D – Rotherham United.

522. Middlesbrough.

523. Three.

524. Trevor Francis.

525. Nottingham Forest and West Ham United.

526. Sporting Braga and Red Star Belgrade.

527. Birmingham City, Norwich City and Swansea City.

528. Johnny Giles.

529. B – Luton Town.

530. Aston Villa, Wolves, Wycombe Wanderers and Chester City.

QUIZ NO 54 - 12 TOP THROSTLES NO 8: WG RICHARDSON

531. C – Hartlepools United.

532. C – Millwall.

533. A – Amsterdam.

534. Nine.

535. 39.

536. Sheffield United and Darlington.

537. Seven.

538. West Ham United.

539. Leicester City and Sunderland.

540. D – Villa Park.

QUIZ NO 55 - 12 TOP THROSTLES NO 9: BOBBY ROBSON

541. Fulham.

542. C – Manchester City.

543. Cardiff City.

544. Leicester City.

545. C – Burnley.

546. B – France.

547. Scotland and Mexico.

548. C – Nottingham Forest.

549. Blackpool.

550. He managed Ipswich Town to a semi-final win over Albion in the FA Cup.

QUIZ NO 56 - 12 TOP THROSTLES NO 10: BRYAN ROBSON

551. B – Bootham Crescent.

552. Cardiff City.

553. D – St Mirren.

554. C – 13.

555. Ipswich Town.

556. C – Norway.

557. Fulham.

558. Lincoln City and Grimsby Town.

559. £1.5 million.

560. True.

QUIZ NO 57 – 12 TOP THROSTLES NO 11: BOB TAYLOR

561. Bristol City.

562. Brentford.

563. 30.

564. Guy Whittingham.

565. Bolton Wanderers and Barnsley.

566. Bobby Gould, Ossie Ardiles and Gary Megson.

567. Luton Town and Northampton Town.

568. Watford.

569. Aylesbury United and Wycombe Wanderers.

570. Coventry City, Rotherham United and Crystal Palace.

QUIZ NO 58 – 12 TOP THROSTLES NO 12: JOHN WILE

571. 500.

572. Peterborough United.

573. B – Blackpool.

574. B – Goodison Park.

575. Inter Milan.

576. D – Upton Park.

577. Seven.

578. Bolton Wanderers and Leeds United.

579. Coventry City.

580. His head is bandaged and it's from Albion's FA Cup semi-final against Ipswich Town in 1978.

QUIZ NO 59 – VENUES

581. The Oval.

582. Molineux and St Andrew's.

583. The Crystal Palace.

584. Highbury.

585. A – Bramall Lane.

586. Villa Park.

587. Wembley.

588. A – Burnden Park.

589. Hillsborough.

590. Old Trafford.

QUIZ NO 60 – WBA IN THE FA CUP 1883-1915

591. D – Wednesbury Town.

592. B – Old Westminsters.

593. B – Blackburn Rovers.

594. A – Chatham.

595. Albion protested about the state of the pitch.

596. C – Stamford Bridge.

597. Southampton.

598. Spurs and Fulham.

599. B – Everton.

600. New Brighton Tower and Southshore, who became Blackpool.

QUIZ NO 61 – WBA IN THE FA CUP 1919-1939

601. D – Notts County.

602. D – Villa Park.

603. Spurs.

604. Aston Villa.

605. D – Wrexham.

606. York City.

607. B – Jimmy Cookson.

608. Sheffield United and Spennymoor United.

609. Stockport County and Manchester United.

610. Portsmouth.

QUIZ NO 62 – WBA IN THE FA CUP 1946-1960

611. Derby County, Charlton Athletic, Wolves and Aston Villa.

612. D – Rotherham United.

613. Dave Walsh.

614. Gateshead.

615. C – Nottingham Forest.

616. Chelsea.

617. Ron Greenwood.

618. Stuart Williams.

619. Manchester.

620. Charlton Athletic and Derby County.

QUIZ NO 63 – WBA IN CUP COMPETITIONS 1960-1970

621. Spurs and Liverpool.

622. Plymouth Argyle.

623. Walsall.

624. Peterborough United, West Ham United and Carlisle United.

625. B – Northampton Town.

626. Lincoln City.

627. Southampton and Portsmouth.

628. Maine Road.

629. They were all London clubs – Fulham, Arsenal and Chelsea.

630. D – Meadow Lane.

QUIZ NO 64 – WBA IN CUP COMPETITIONS 1970-1980

631. Spurs.

632. Nottingham Forest.

633. Tony Brown.

634. Fulham.

635. Southampton, Ipswich Town and West Ham United.

636. Sheffield United and Exeter City.

637. Carlisle United.

638. The replay was also at the Hawthorns because Elland Road had been closed by the authorities.

639. C – Maine Road.

640. Manchester United.

QUIZ NO 65 – WBA IN CUP COMPETITIONS 1980-1990

641. Five.

642. Millwall.

643. Bradford City.

644. Wimbledon.

645. Imre Varadi.

646. C – Derby County.

647. Coventry City.

648. Spurs and Aston Villa.

649. West Ham United and Crystal Palace.

650. Plymouth Argyle.

QUIZ NO 66 - WBA IN CUP COMPETITIONS 1990-2000

651. 12.

652. Woking.

653. Marlow.

654. A – Kevin Donovan.

655. Coventry City, Crewe Alexandra and Chelsea.

656. Richard Sneekes.

657. They were the only three away grounds on which Albion played in both domestic cup competitions.

658. Bristol Rovers.

659. Chelsea in 1996-97.

660. Goodman and Shakespeare.

QUIZ NO 67 - WBA IN THE FOOTBALL LEAGUE 1888-1900

661. Stoke.

662. Bolton Wanderers.

663. Fifth.

664. B – 5-4.

665. Sunderland and Notts County.

666. Wolves and Everton.

667. Sheffield Wednesday.

668. They came through the test matches that decided who went up and down, winning two and drawing one of their four games against Manchester City and Liverpool.

669. Billy Bassett.

670. Nottingham.

QUIZ NO 68 - WBA IN THE FOOTBALL LEAGUE 1900-1915

671. They won 3-2 at Preston North End.

672. 17.

673. Eight.

674. 4,000.

675. Liverpool.

676. Spurs.

677. D – Fred Shinton.

678. Fred Buck.

679. Bentley and Morris.

680. Joe Dorsett.

QUIZ NO 69 - WBA IN THE FOOTBALL LEAGUE 1919-1930

681. 104.

682. Fred Morris.

683. Blackburn Rovers and Huddersfield Town.

684. A – Bobby Blood.

685. Huddersfield Town and George James.

686. West Ham United.

687. Aston Villa.

688. Jimmy Cookson.

689. A – Chelsea.

690. Hull City and Millwall.

QUIZ NO 70 - WBA IN THE FOOTBALL LEAGUE 1930-1939

691. Spurs.

692. A – Cardiff City

693. Raw, Richardson and Robbins.

694. Sunderland.

695. D – Maine Road.

696. C – Derby County.

697. Aston Villa and Blackburn Rovers.

698. B – Jack Mahon.

699. Manchester City.

700. B – 3,109.

QUIZ NO 71 – WBA IN THE FOOTBALL LEAGUE 1946-1960

701. Dave Walsh.

702. Ike Clarke.

703. Arthur Rowley.

704. Fulham.

705. B – Charlton Athletic.

706. C – St James' Park.

707. Wolves.

708. Johnny Nicholls.

709. Don Howe.

710. Manchester City.

QUIZ NO 72 – WBA IN THE FOOTBALL LEAGUE 1960-1970

711. B – Alec Jackson.

712. B – Blackpool

713. Brisbane Road, home of Leyton Orient.

714. Michael Fudge.

715. Bobby Cram.

716. C – Newcastle United.

717. Burnley.

718. Colin Suggett.

719. Manchester United.

720. Clive Clark.

QUIZ NO 73 – WBA IN THE FOOTBALL LEAGUE 1970-1980

721. Bobby Gould.

722. Ally and Tony Brown.

723. Crystal Palace.

724. Blackpool.

725. Bristol City and Bolton Wanderers.

726. Ipswich Town.

727. Huddersfield Town.

728. Coventry City and Manchester United.

729. Six.

730. Remi Moses and Peter Barnes.

QUIZ NO 74 – WBA IN THE FOOTBALL LEAGUE 1980-1990

731. Regis and King.

732. Martin Jol.

733. Romeo Zondervan.

734. Gary Thompson.

735. Birmingham City.

736. Imre Varadi.

737. Don Goodman.

738. Tony Morley.

739. David Moyes.

740. Barnsley.

QUIZ NO 75 – WBA IN THE FOOTBALL LEAGUE 1990-2000

741. Gary Bannister.

742. Exeter City.

743. Alan Dickens and Craig Shakespeare.

744. Andy Hunt.

745. Birmingham City.

746. Lee Ashcroft.

747. Paul Peschisolido.

748. Kevin Kilbane.

749. Lee Hughes.

750. True.

QUIZ NO 76 - WBA SEASON 2000-2001

751. Lee Hughes.

752. Bolton Wanderers, Preston North End and Birmingham City.

753. Derby County.

754. C – Swansea City.

755. Jason Roberts.

756. Neil Clement.

757. Richard Sneekes.

758. Jason van Blerk.

759. Portsmouth.

760. Barnsley.

QUIZ NO 77 - WBA SEASON 2001-2002

761. 29.

762. Scott Dobie.

763. C – Rotherham United.

764. Crystal Palace.

765. Fulham and Charlton Athletic.

766. Sunderland and Swindon Town.

767. C – Russell Hoult.

768. Neil Clement.

769. Cheltenham Town.

770. Portsmouth.

QUIZ NO 78 - WBA SEASON 2002-2003

771. Old Trafford.

772. Sean Gregan.

773. C – Lee Marshall.

774. Fulham.

775. Watford and Wigan Athletic.

776. A – Bradford City.

777. Danny Dichio.

778. Jason Koumas.

779. Geoff Horsfield.

780. Five.

QUIZ NO 79 - WBA SEASON 2003-2004

781. Norwich City.

782. West Ham United.

783. Rob Hulse.

784. Jason Koumas.

785. C – Nottingham Forest.

786. Brentford and Arsenal.

787. Hartlepool United and Newcastle United.

788. Bernt Haas, Lee Hughes and Rob Hulse.

789. Thomas Gaardsøe.

790. Lee Hughes.

QUIZ NO 80 - WBA SEASON 2004-2005

791. Portsmouth.

792. Southampton were relegated.

793. Rob Earnshaw.

794. Charlton Athletic.

795. Colchester United.

796. Paul Robinson.

797. Preston North End and Spurs.

798. Nwankwo Kanu – he was an ex-Arsenal man.

799. Ronnie Wallwork.

800. Zoltán Gera.

QUIZ NO 81 – WBA SEASON 2005-2006

801. Sunderland.

802. Wigan Athletic.

803. Martin Albrechtsen.

804. Jonathan Greening.

805. Geoff Horsfield.

806. Nathan Ellington and Zoltán Gera.

807. Richard Chaplow.

808. Nwankwo Kanu.

809. Blackburn Rovers.

810. Manchester United.

QUIZ NO 82 – WBA SEASON 2006-2007

811. Manchester United.

812. Five games – four wins.

813. Diomansy Kamara.

814. Leeds United and Middlesbrough.

815. Leyton Orient and Arsenal.

816. Nathan Ellington and Stuart Nicholson.

817. A – Darren Carter.

818. Ipswich Town.

819. Barnsley.

820. Paul Robinson.

QUIZ NO 83 – WBA SEASON 2007-2008

821. Tony Mowbray and Kevin Phillips.

822. Jonathan Greening.

823. True.

824. QPR.

825. Peterborough United.

826. Jonathan Greening, Kevin Phillips and Paul Robinson.

827. C – Ishmael Miller.

828. Coventry City and Bristol Rovers.

829. Nwankwo Kanu.

830. Stoke City.

QUIZ NO 84 – WBA SEASON 2008-2009

831. Celtic.

832. Middlesbrough.

833. Chris Brunt.

834. Burnley.

835. Gianni Zuiverloon.

836. Hartlepool United.

837. Robert Koren.

838. Spurs.

839. Middlesbrough and Newcastle United.

840. The Halfords Lane Stand.

QUIZ NO 85 – WBA SEASON 2009-2010

841. Milton Keynes Dons.

842. Seven.

843. Newcastle United.

844. Jonas Olsson.

845. Graham Dorrans.

846. Huddersfield Town and Rotherham United.

847. Arsenal and Reading.

848. Norwich City.

849. Graham Dorrans.

850. Nine players scored but no one who scored in the first game did so in the second.

QUIZ NO 86 – WBA SEASON 2010-2011

851. Chelsea and 11th.

852. Roy Hodgson – Liverpool.

853. Reading.

854. Leyton Orient and Leicester City.

855. Chris Brunt scored with two penalties.

856. Youssouf Mulumbu.

857. Carlos Vela.

858. Nicky Shorey.

859. Peter Odemwingie.

860. Somen Tchoyi.

QUIZ NO 87 – WBA SEASON 2011-2012

861. Ten.

862. Manchester United, Arsenal and Steven Reid.

863. 1978-79.

864. Simon Cox and Rob Earnshaw.

865. Bournemouth and Everton.

866. Jonas Olsson.

867. Sunderland.

868. Ben Foster.

869. Demba Ba and Paul Scharner.

870. Martin and Jonas Olsson.

QUIZ NO 88 – WBA SEASON 2012-2013

871. Third.

872. 17.

873. Shane Long.

874. D – QPR.

875. Yeovil Town.

876. Manchester City.

877. Gareth McAuley.

878. B – the 1980s.

879. 14.

880. (a) 5-2 to Manchester United; (b) 5-5; (c) Romelu Lukaku; (d) Jonas Olsson.

QUIZ NO 89 – WBA SEASON 2013-2014

881. Ben Foster.

882. B – Arsenal and Crystal Palace.

883. Newport County and Saido Berahino.

884. Gareth McAuley.

885. Spurs.

886. Stéphane Sessègnon.

887. Seven.

888. Shane Long.

889. Lugano.

890. Morgan Amalfitano, Nicolas Anelka and Victor Anichebe.

QUIZ NO 90 – WBA SEASON 2014-2015

891. Alan Irvine departed and Tony Pulis came in.

892. Romelu Lukaku.

893. Craig Gardner.

894. Gateshead.

895. QPR.

896. Saido Berahino.

897. Joleon Lescott.

898. Jonas Olsson.

899. Boaz Myhill saved Robin van Persie's penalty.

900. West Ham United, Birmingham City and Aston Villa.

QUIZ NO 91 - WBR SEASON 2015-2016

901. Darren Fletcher and Craig Dawson.

902. Salomón Rondón.

903. Jonny Evans.

904. Heurelho Gomes saved Saido Berahino's penalties.

905. Bristol City and Reading.

906. C – Norwich City.

907. Stoke City.

908. Craig Dawson and Jonas Olsson.

909. Jonny Evans.

910. Spurs.

QUIZ NO 92 - WBR SEASON 2016-2017

911. Ben Foster.

912. Hal Robson-Kanu.

913. Gareth Barry and Romelu Lukaku.

914. Nacer Chadli.

915. Swansea City.

916. Shane Long and Virgil van Dijk.

917. Gareth McAuley.

918. Derby County.

919. Arsenal.

920. It gave Chelsea the Premier League title.

QUIZ NO 93 - WBR SEASON 2017-2018

921. Salomón Rondón and Jay Rodriguez.

922. Ahmed Hegazi.

923. Tony Pulis.

924. Brighton & Hove Albion.

925. Eight.

926. Exeter City and Accrington Stanley.

927. Southampton.

928. James McClean scored the own goal and Jay Rodriguez equalised from the spot.

929. Jake Livermore.

930. Five.

QUIZ NO 94 - WBR SEASON 2018-2019

931. Dwight Gayle and Chris Brunt.

932. Luton Town and Mansfield Town.

933. Brighton & Hove Albion and Crystal Palace.

934. Harvey Barnes.

935. Rotherham United and Preston North End.

936. Jay Rodriguez.

937. QPR.

938. Sam Johnstone.

939. Barry and Gibbs.

940. Jimmy Shan.

QUIZ NO 95 – WBA SEASON 2019-2020

941. Leeds United.
942. Grady Diangana.
943. Ken Zohore.
944. Charlie Austin.
945. Barnsley.
946. Semi Ajayi.
947. D – 19.
948. Charlton Athletic, West Ham United and Millwall.
949. San Johnstone played every Championship game and Matheus Pereira was player of the year.
950. Brentford.

QUIZ NO 96 – WBA SEASON 2020-2021

951. Fulham and Sheffield United.
952. Chelsea by 5-2.
953. Matheus Pereira.
954. Aston Villa and Jake Livermore.
955. Semi Ajayi and Mbaye Diagne.
956. Sam Johnstone.
957. Leeds United, Manchester City and Arsenal.
958. Blackpool and Brentford.
959. Harrogate Town.
960. Valérien Ismaël and Barnsley.

QUIZ NO 97 – WBA SEASON 2021-2022

961. The 11th game – at Stoke City.
962. Robinson.
963. Alex Mowatt and Semi Ajayi.

964. Brighton.
965. 6-0.
966. Karlan Grant.
967. Karlan Grant and Andy Carroll.
968. The matches repeated scorelines from FA Cup finals – against Blackburn Rovers in 1886 and Barnsley in 1912.
969. Cardiff City.
970. Kyle McFadzean.

QUIZ NO 98 – WBA SEASON 2022-2023

971. Steve Bruce, Hull City and 5-2.
972. Richard Beale and Carlos Corberán.
973. Coventry City.
974. Huddersfield Town.
975. Sheffield United and Derby County.
976. Chesterfield and Brandon Thomas-Asante.
977. Bristol City.
978. Tom Rogic.
979. Jay Rodriguez for Burnley.
980. Swansea City.

QUIZ NO 99 – WHERE DID YOU COME FROM?

981. Osasuna.
982. AZ Alkmaar.
983. Locomotiv Moscow.
984. Shanghai Shenhua.
985. Zenit Saint Petersburg.
986. Racing Club de Avellaneda.
987. Rosenborg.

988. PSG.

989. Werder Bremen.

990. Benfica.

QUIZ NO 100 - WILD CARD

991. 6-5.

992. John Trewick.

993. Jack Haines.

994. Ron Saunders and Steve Bruce.

995. Lee Hughes in 1998-99.

996. Leeds United.

997. Enzo Maresca.

998. Ally Brown, Peter Barnes and Tony Brown.

999. Darren Moore and Luke Moore.

1000. Win the FA Cup as players with two different clubs – the other manager to do this is Johnny Giles.

BACK COVER ANSWERS

1. Roy Hodgson and Sam Allardyce.

2. Osvaldo Ardiles and Nobby Stiles.

3. Brian Talbot, Stuart Pearson and Johnny Giles.

Printed in Great Britain
by Amazon

35435496R00069